0065107

DATE DUE

THE JUMP ROPE PRIMER

Ken M. Solis, MD
Ropics®, Inc.

Bill Budris, BS
Victory Elementary School, Milwaukee, WI
Wizard Jump Rope Demonstration Team Coordinator

Human Kinetics Books
Champaign, Illinois

Library of Congress Cataloging-in-Publication Data

Solis, Ken M., 1958-
  The jump rope primer / by Ken M. Solis and Bill Budris.
    p. cm.
  Includes bibliographical references and index.
  ISBN 0-87322-302-0
  1. Rope skipping.   I. Budris, Bill, 1946-   . II. Title.
GV498.S65   1991
796.2--dc20   90-45347
                                                         CIP

ISBN: 0-87322-302-0

Acquisitions Editor: Rick Frey, PhD
Developmental Editor: Holly Gilly
Assistant Editors: Valerie Hall, Robert King, Dawn Levy
Copyeditor: Wendy Nelson
Proofreader: Phaedra Hargis
Production Director: Ernie Noa
Typesetter: Sandra Meier
Text Design: Keith Blomberg
Text Layout: Denise Lowry
Cover Design: Jack Davis
Cover Photo/Interior Photos: Dean Johnson
Printer: Versa Press

Human Kinetics books are available at special discounts for bulk purchase for sales promotions, premiums, fund-raising, or educational use. Special editions or book excerpts can also be created to specification. For details, contact the Special Sales Manager at Human Kinetics.

Printed in the United States of America

10 9 8 7 6 5 4 3 2 1

Human Kinetics Books
A Division of Human Kinetics Publishers, Inc.
Box 5076, Champaign, IL 61825-5076
1-800-747-4457

UK Office:
Human Kinetics Publishers (UK) Ltd.
PO Box 18
Rawdon, Leeds LS19 6TG
England
(0532) 504211

It's only fitting that our first book should be dedicated
to the "first" people in our lives: Deb and Barb.

Contents

Preface

In the war against our society's flagging state of physical fitness, the enemy's chief officer is General Inactivity. Across the country, physical educators are facing an assault from General Inactivity's powerful TV-video alliance on one front while battling shrinking budgets on the other. Coaches grapple not only with teaching the many aspects of their sports, but also with getting their less active recruits into competitive physical condition. Evidence continues to accumulate that obesity and other afflictions usually associated with middle age and beyond are increasingly besieging our youth. In summary, despite the much-trumpeted fitness boom, America's youth and adults are less fit than ever.

The booby traps with which General Inactivity repeatedly snares his casualties have many names, but they can often be recognized by such tags as *automatic*, *electronic*, and *motorized*. For example, automatic clothes washers have replaced washboards and elbow grease. Electronic versions of Tag and Cops-and-Robbers, using buttons and joysticks, give kids less reason to run around the yard. And jaunts to the corner store or the third floor are now taken in motorized cars and elevators, respectively.

If we are to advance against General Inactivity, we must fight the battle with tools that are convenient and efficient. And to overcome our charges' reluctance to engage in anything that might be perceived as work, the activity must be enjoyable and make them feel good about themselves. *The Jump Rope Primer* explains and teaches an exercise alternative that not only fits the bill, but, unlike most Pentagon projects, exceeds the original specifications. Here's a brief preview of some of the "specs" that make rope jumping such an attractive addition to anyone's fitness armamentarium:

Benefits of Rope Jumping

- **Promotes total fitness.** Scientifically proven to be an unsurpassed developer of aerobic conditioning, rope jumping also promotes other important areas of fitness such as strength, quickness, agility, coordination, timing, rhythm, and kinesthetic awareness.

- **Versatile.** Rope jumping can be done indoors or out, alone or in groups, at home or on the road, by young and old, and used for recreation, exercise, athletic training, and even entertainment.

- **Variety.** Literally hundreds of techniques exist with the short rope alone. Add the possibilities with long ropes and partner jumping, and the number increases tenfold.

- **Accessible to everyone.** In addition to offering a smorgasbord in fitness development and options, the jump rope is also the McDonald's of convenience. The necessary equipment fits any budget or storage room, and apparel and facilities are readily available.

- **Safe.** A common misconception is that rope jumping is hard on the knees. Actually, research has shown that the impact of basic rope jumping is less than one half the impact of running. More importantly, because rope jumping involves virtually no sudden unpredictable movements or collisions with other participants, serious injuries are extremely rare.

- **Fun!** Of course, any exercise is nearly worthless if it doesn't produce a good feeling inside when practiced. Fortunately, you don't have to convince young people that rope jumping is fun; millions already do it without coaxing. Turn on some music and everyone gets hooked.

Despite these weighty virtues, rope jumping is not without its detractors. Many complain that it is too demanding physically, is difficult to master, and lacks stimulating goals. All these objections have at least some merit against the traditional approach. *The Jump Rope Primer* offers a unique program called Ropics®, which addresses these objections by extensively employing one guiding principle—*graduation*—defined by *Webster's New World Dictionary* as "an arrangement or classification into grades according to amount, size, quality, etc." Applied to rope jumping, graduation means slowly increasing exercise intensity so that even novices can begin without getting discouraging aches, pains, and strains. It means teaching skills step by step so that no participants label themselves "klutzes." Graduation also means dividing the innumerable and varied techniques according to degree of difficulty—to both extend guidance and provide motivating goals.

The Primer is designed to give physical education teachers, fitness instructors, and coaches a solid foundation of knowledge about rope jumping. This book therefore also gives information on

- different types of jump ropes,
- preferred floor surfaces,
- relevant stretching techniques,
- class and program design,
- jump rope games, and
- tournaments and other events that motivate students.

This information is derived from both hard-won experience and the findings of scientific research.

In summary, *The Jump Rope Primer* sheds light on a piece of exercise equipment that has been frequently misunderstood and underestimated. You'll come to realize that rope jumping is one of the most versatile and effective ways to increase physical fitness and should not be overlooked in our ongoing war against General Inactivity.

Acknowledgments

We would like to thank the members of the jump rope team The Wizards for the time and effort they spent modeling for this book: Lee Borchardt, Ryan Fula, Jessica Hogan, Tony Janke, Felicia Kertzman, Kris Mazola, Cari Piontek, Neal Rozga, Bob Stenzel, Tiffany Weisling, and the Michalski sisters—Christa, Lisa, and Laura. Their talent and patience is much appreciated.

In a book with over 150 photographs, special thanks is also due to our photographer, Dean Johnson, who went the extra mile (of film) to make it all work.

Finally, despite the availability of computerized spell-checkers and grammar correctors, we thank Deb Solis, Barb Budris, Kathleen Hargarten, MD, and Judy Clark for their valuable input, insights, and corrections.

I PART

An Introduction to Rope Jumping and the Ropics® Program

Because this book is a primer, we want to start with the basics. The first four chapters give an overview of rope jumping. Chapter 1 examines the history of this increasingly diverse activity and lists organizations dedicated to promoting it. Chapter 2 reviews the numerous benefits and advantages of rope jumping as a form of aerobic exercise. Despite rope jumping's many strengths, it does have a few weaknesses. Chapter 3 introduces a new program called *Ropics* that is designed to make rope jumping come a little closer to perfection. Part I ends with chapter 4, which gives valuable practical information on such matters as jump ropes, floor surfaces, and musical accompaniment.

1
CHAPTER

Rope Jumping Yesterday, Today, and Tomorrow

In the realm of game and sport, rope jumping is one of the most enduring and widespread activities people do, and its popularity continues to grow.

A Brief History

The exact origins of rope jumping, or rope skipping, are unknown, but it probably dates back to ancient times and a variety of cultures. According to one theory, ancient Egyptian and Chinese rope makers twirled and jumped over their ropes to recover loose strands of hemp. Children imitated the practice for fun, and sailors later spread the idea on their distant voyages. Soon young people all over the world were "rope jumping," using whatever material happened to be handy. Swedes jumped over ropes made of wicker, Hungarians over plaited straw, and Spaniards, leather thongs.

Rope jumping was probably introduced to America in the 1600s by the Dutch settlers of New Amsterdam (modern-day New York City). To this day, some of the best "Double Dutch" rope jumpers in the world come from there. (Double Dutch is a rope jumping variation where two long ropes are alternately turned inward by persons at each end; see page 53.) It may surprise you that until the turn of the 20th century, rope jumping was primarily a boys' game. Then boys began to pursue team sports, and rope jumping became the domain of two other groups. Young girls jumped rope for fun to many singsong rhymes. Athletes such as

boxers jumped rope to train their bodies for the rigors of their sports.

By the 1960s, luminaries like Paul Smith and Frank Prentup were promoting rope jumping as a great way for nearly anyone to have fun *and* train the body to become fit. Around the same time, *aerobic exercise* became a buzz word, thanks to Dr. Kenneth Cooper, its "father." Soon the nation's roads were sprinkled with runners, walkers, and bicyclists, and health clubs sprouted to cater to swimmers, racquetball players, and aerobic dancers. The word was out that these aerobic exercises could burn excess fat, improve overall vigor, and decrease the risk of heart disease—the number one cause of death in Western society. Research also supported Smith's and Prentup's contention by proving that rope jumping was among this company of beneficial aerobic exercises.

Rope Jumping Today

The 1970s to 1990s have witnessed the greatest growth and development of rope jumping yet. Before the late 1970s, jump rope enthusiasts were hard-pressed to find any jump rope–related event or organization. But several organizations and events have come into existence, and all are experiencing steady growth in membership and international participation. Events and organizations are important for the development of any activity, because they provide forums for the exchange of ideas and a sense of camaraderie for participants.

Jump Rope For Heart (JRFH)

In 1978, Jean Barkow, a physical education teacher at Riverside University High School in Milwaukee, Wisconsin, had an inspiration: Why not educate children about the benefits of aerobic exercise through an activity they already like? And how about raising some money for heart research in the meantime? She approached the American Heart Association with the idea. They liked it.

Today, JRFH is the largest event in rope jumping and one of the most successful charity fundraisers ever. Cosponsored by the American Alliance for Health, Physical Education, Recreation and Dance (AAHPERD) to benefit the American Heart Association (AHA), JRFH raised $24.7 million and involved 1.2 million participants from over 13,500 schools during the 1989-1990 school year alone. The success of JRFH is due to several factors:

- It raises money to study a disease that in some way touches nearly every family.
- AAHPERD and AHA supply volunteer organizers with excellent educational materials and offer rewards for successful fund-raisers.
- Perhaps most importantly, JRFH is fun and exciting for everyone from the school principal to the elementary-aged student.

Here's a brief review of what all the excitement is about:

Before the day of the event, participants obtain pledges from sponsors to donate a certain amount of money for each minute their teams continuously jump rope. The organizers may also opt to educate the participants before the event about the benefits of aerobic exercise and how to properly jump rope. On the big day, teams of six take turns jumping rope for up to 3 hours straight. The participants are free to do tricks, play jump rope games, and use long or short ropes.

Some of the most prolific sources for ideas on tricks are jump rope teams with names like "Hot Dog USA," "The Red Hots," and "The High Fliers." These are just a few of the hundreds of demonstration teams, spread all over the country, that travel to promote healthy lifestyles and increase enthusiasm for JRFH at schools and other institutions. After one of their fast-paced, incredibly varied shows, nary a student isn't scrambling for a jump rope during the next recess. Suddenly video games look boring; the notion that rope jumping is for "sissies" has been swept away.

For more information on JRFH- or AHA-sponsored demonstration teams, contact your nearest AHA office.

International Rope Skipping Organization (IRSO)

The Skip-Its, a team from Boulder, Colorado, formed in 1976, was AHA's first demonstration team. In 1982 its pioneering founder, Richard Cendali, also organized and began directing IRSO. IRSO currently draws its 5,000-plus members from several countries. Most members are from demonstration teams of the United States, but any enthusiast can join to take advantage of their newsletter, annual camps, and competitions.

In each regional or international competition, there are speed, compulsory, and freestyle events for both Double Dutch and single rope jumping (see chapter 9 for an outline of the tournament format). Age-group divisions range from second grade and below to ninth grade and above. The regional and international camps are designed to teach anyone from beginner to advanced an amazing spectrum of techniques with both long and short ropes. IRSO also has an international demonstration team that travels worldwide to promote rope jumping.

For more information, contact
International Rope Skipping Organization
P.O. Box 3307
Boulder, CO 80307
(303) 530-7179

Canadian Skipping Association (CSA)

CSA is the Canadian equivalent of IRSO and has similar objectives. The association began in 1985 and became registered with the Canadian Amateur Athletic Association in 1989. CSA acts as a governing body for the sport of rope skipping in Canada and promotes rope skipping as a beneficial form of exercise and recreation. An informative newsletter is available to its growing membership, and CSA also has liability insurance available for team members.

Unlike IRSO, which holds its camps in conjunction with competitions, CSA holds its major competition at the end of May and its camp in July or August. The 5-day camp, like IRSO's, is designed to teach enthusiasts and teachers the many possibilities in rope jumping. Anyone interested may attend. CSA has a national team that makes trips to other countries, such as Germany and Australia, to spread the word about fitness and health—jump-rope style.

For more information, contact
Canadian Skipping Association
P.O. Box 7165
Ancaster, Ontario L9G 3L4
Canada
(416) 648-0302

American Double Dutch League (ADDL)

Unlike IRSO and CSA, which promote nearly all types of rope jumping, ADDL specializes in Double Dutch. Founded in 1973 by two police detectives, David Walker and Ulysses Williams, ADDL draws its membership from schools, YMCAs, 4-H clubs, the Girl Scouts, and city park and recreation departments. Each year up to 250,000 young people do their best freestyle Double Dutch routines at regional meets to vie for the opportunity to go to the summer international competition. The creativity, athleticism, and teamwork displayed by these "Double Dutchers" have frequently been acclaimed by the media, and several of the talented championship teams have been featured in commercials for McDonald's. ADDL state representatives, coaches, and coordinators meet each fall for the ADDL Conference.

For more information, contact
American Double Dutch League
Montgomery T. Gardner
National Program Manager
4220 Eads Street, N.E.
Washington, DC 20019

Washington State Records Day

Since 1983, Bob Melson, coach of the Hot Dog USA demonstration jump rope team, has organized an annual State Records Day. The event is held on the last weekend in January and attracts about 300 jumpers from the Pacific Northwest. The event challenges children from seven age divisions to beat records in 10 events, including the most jumps in 1 minute, the most consecutive Double Unders, and the most jumps on a pogo stick without a miss.

Records Day is great fun and spurs children to strive for concrete goals. It also exemplifies the great diversity of goals available in rope jumping—there is something in it for everyone.

For more information, contact
Washington State Records Day
c/o Bob Melson
4414 Woodland Park Avenue North
Seattle, WA 98103

Bloomer Speed-Jumping Competition

Bloomer, a small town in Northern Wisconsin, may have the oldest rope jumping event anywhere. Since 1960, speed-jumping specialists from Wisconsin and Minnesota have gathered in this self-proclaimed jump rope capital of the world on the last Saturday of each January to compete. The competition is limited to jumping as fast as possible for 10 seconds with a plain hemp rope. Because longer ropes have a longer revolution time, the ropes are shorter than usual, and the participants jump in a semi-crouched position. In the 1989 competition, about 250 jumpers entered the six divisions (spanning preschoolers through senior adults). Spectators never cease to be amazed by the blur of rope and feet created by these speed demons.

For more information, contact
Bloomer Chamber of Commerce
P.O. Box 81
Bloomer, WI 54724

Ropics®, Inc.

The Ropics program is the unique jump rope program featured in this book. Ken Solis began developing it in 1980 when he realized that by not restricting yourself to constantly jumping over the rope, you can immensely increase variety and decrease aerobic intensity. Other innovations have been added to Ropics over the ensuing years due to Dr. Solis's continued work and the contributions of his partner, Kathleen Hargarten, MD. Ropics, Inc., their company, also offers workshops, demonstrations, and professional-level entertainment for schools and other organizations. Ropics, Inc., has also developed an instructor course to give educators the skills and knowledge needed to teach rope jumping. Continued support for instructors is provided with a regular newsletter, access to jump rope-related materials, and more advanced workshops.

For more information, contact
Ropics, Inc.
P.O. Box 373
Greendale, WI 53129
(414) 423-1707

The Future

Rope jumping is becoming increasingly popular, and soon there won't be any stopping it. Each year, millions of children learn through the JRFH event about the fun and incredible variety hidden in a simple length of rope. Aerobic dancers are beginning to look at the jump rope as a way to add diversity and new challenges to their workouts. College and professional basketball, football, tennis, and other sport programs are using the jump rope for cross-training. Rhythmic gymnastics, a women's Olympic sport that ingeniously incorporates the jump rope with dance and gymnastics techniques, is becoming increasingly popular with both participants and spectators. One day rope jumping may be an Olympic sport in its own right.

Why the optimism? Let's look at its strengths.

2
CHAPTER

The Benefits and Advantages of Rope Jumping

Aerobic dance, power walking, circuit training, and triathlons are all aerobic activities that became known to most people only a few years ago. But nothing surpasses the venerable jump rope for developing total fitness, promoting self-esteem, and convenience. Most significantly, children who balk at the thought of exercise eagerly jump rope, because they consider it to be something much more important—play!

Develops Total Fitness

Physical fitness is not an all-or-nothing phenomenon. It is a combination of various factors that influence our health and how well we cope with work. Experts seem to agree that aerobic, or cardiovascular, conditioning has the single greatest influence on our well-being; also important are weight control and the strength and flexibility of the musculoskeletal system. Fitness doesn't stop there, however, especially for athletes. Quickness, coordination, agility, and timing are just some of the other critical elements of "total fitness." Few activities address the concept of total fitness better than rope jumping.

Aerobic Conditioning

Aerobic conditioning refers to the changes that occur in the cardiovascular system (heart and circulation), pulmonary system (lungs), and muscular system in response to exercises that repetitively use large muscle groups. Specifically, the heart becomes larger and pumps stronger; the diaphragm,

which powers the lungs, increases in endurance; and the circulation and efficiency of the muscles improve dramatically. These changes are optimized when aerobic exercises are done for at least 20 minutes three to five times a week, at an intensity that increases the heart rate to 60%-85% of its maximum. The practical, immediate result of these changes is increased stamina for normal daily activities. The long-term payoff is a decreased risk of heart disease, diabetes, obesity, depression, high blood pressure, and possibly colon cancer. Not surprisingly, life span, self-confidence, and vigor increase also.

Rope jumping qualifies as an aerobic exercise because it readily meets all the criteria just mentioned. In 1968 John Baker published a study claiming that rope jumping was 3 times as efficient as running in developing aerobic conditioning; subsequent, more sophisticated, studies have proven, however, that rope jumping is essentially equivalent to running and other aerobic exercises in developing this important quality. The real strength of rope jumping over many other exercises is that it has many benefits in addition to aerobic conditioning.

Stronger Muscles and Bones

The body has a straightforward rule: Use it or lose it. This is especially true for muscles, which turn weak and flaccid if not used. The converse is that they also quickly become stronger and firmer if exercised—regardless of age. Rope jumping uses the muscles of the calves, thighs, and buttocks for jumping; the shoulders, arms, and forearms for turning the rope; and the abdomen, chest, upper back, and hip flexors for executing many of the more advanced techniques. Thus, essentially all major muscle groups can benefit from this exercise. Of course, the jump rope won't build large muscles like a set of weights can, but it will give them the endurance, firmness, and strength needed for life's everyday challenges.

Bones also respond to exercise, by becoming denser and stronger. In fact, research has shown that regular exercise is one of the most promising hedges against osteoporosis, or "brittle bones"—a debilitating and painful malady of old age that may be averted by exercising regularly before the condition occurs.

Speed

In many sports, speed is valued more highly than strength. All the muscles of a superhero won't do much good if your opponent just left you at the scrimmage line after a sudden fake to the left and a bolt down the field. Even activities that seem to rely on strength, such as shot putting, are more often dependent on *power*, which is the product of strength *and* speed. Once mastered, rope jumping can be done at lightning-like speeds as well as at casual rates, so experienced jumpers have the option of developing the quick hands and fast feet needed for many sports. Boxers have known this all along.

Motor Skills

Strong, quick muscles won't reach their full potential, though, if the motor centers that orchestrate their movements aren't primed. In this regard, rope jumping is similar to dance and gymnastics, disciplines that develop a wide range of upper and lower body motor skills. Rope jumping even has some significant advantages over these high-profile disciplines. Self-conscious boys usually accept rope jumping much quicker than dance. Rope jumping is safer than gymnastics because it doesn't put the limbs, neck, and head at risk. The equipment, as well as the liability insurance, is also much less expensive. Finally, although rope jumping requires proper instruction, as does any skilled activity, the jump rope itself does a fair amount of coaching, because a "miss" automatically tells the participant that the movement wasn't done correctly.

Gross Coordination

The immense diversity of jump rope techniques, which require the precise movement and coopera-

tion of arms and legs, ensures that gross coordination can be refined indefinitely. Many movements can be duplicated without a rope (e.g., High Steps, explained on page 37). Adding this versatile piece of equipment to the movement, however, increases the challenge, interest, and required accuracy.

Agility

Agility is the ability to move or change position quickly and deftly. It relies on a combination of dynamic balance, coordination, and having the lower body strength to move well on the feet. All of these qualities are developed through the many footwork techniques of rope jumping. So, rather than setting up rows of tires to run through, consider using a few ropes; they're not as heavy, and they're much more versatile.

Timing

Timing is the ability to execute a move at precisely the right moment. Rope jumping can enhance one's sense of timing, because so many techniques require it for successful completion. For example, Side Straddles, or Jumping Jacks, are familiar to most students from calisthenics. Side Straddles with the rope require more exact timing, however, because the feet must be apart only when the rope is overhead. Likewise, with Front Crosses (see page 38) the arms must be fully crossed as the rope approaches that critical zone under the feet.

Rhythm

Rhythm refers to the regular recurrence of movement in time. For many techniques, the challenge lies not in acquiring a new level of coordination or agility, but in learning a new rhythm. For example, the Jump-Bounce (page 27, Figure 5.6), the Two-Foot Jump (page 28, Figure 5.7), and Double Unders (page 80, Figure E.2) require exactly the same skills except that each requires a different rhythm: With the "Jump-Bounce" the rope turns *once* for every *two* jumps. With the Two-Foot Jump the rope turns *once* for each jump, and with Double Unders the rope turns *twice* for each jump. The rhythm variations don't stop there. And note that, again, both upper and lower extremities are involved.

Kinesthetic Awareness

For a professional dancer, it's vital to know exactly how the hands, elbows, feet, head, and other body parts are moving and positioned in space throughout a routine. This ability to sense the movement and position of body parts (without looking) is kinesthetic awareness. The muscles, joints, and possibly tendons all contain nerve endings that convey this information back to the brain. As in dance, only a very few jump rope techniques require eye-hand or eye-foot coordination. Most depend on one's ability to sense exactly where the feet, hands, or other body parts are in relation to the rope or each other.

Weight Control

Obesity is linked not only to self-image problems in our appearance-conscious society, but also to several diseases, such as arthritis, gallstones, high blood pressure, diabetes, and certain types of cancer. Once one is overweight, it's difficult to lose and keep off the excess fat regardless of strategy. However, combining dieting with aerobic exercise is more effective and healthier than dieting alone, for several reasons:

- Calorie output is increased while intake is decreased.
- The drop in basal metabolic rate that occurs with strict dieting is minimized or even reversed.
- Muscle breakdown can be greatly diminished.

All aerobic exercises are good at burning calories, and rope jumping is no exception. At usual rope jumping rates (125 to 140 jumps per minute) a student will burn about 0.086 calories per pound per minute. Therefore, an 80-pound student will burn about 7 calories in 1 minute or 105 calories in 15 minutes of basic rope jumping. Higher jumping speeds or tricks increase the calorie-burning rate even further.

Of course, prevention is immeasurably better than cure. People become overweight due to inactivity more often than overeating, so regular rope jumping or other exercise takes on another degree of importance.

Flexibility

In general, aerobic exercises do little to increase flexibility. This important component of fitness is best attained through proper stretching exercises like those illustrated on pages 63-65. As a rule, slow static stretches are safer and more effective than bouncing or forcefully extending the muscles. Rope jumping lets one use the flexibility attained through stretching, however, with techniques like the Cancan, Step-Throughs, and several others described in Part II.

Relieves Stress and Boosts Self-Esteem

It can be difficult to sell young people on the health benefits of exercise because the sedentary diseases, which might not strike until age 50 or later, seem like an eternity away to them. However, today's youth, as well as adults, can relate to emotional problems like stress, anxiety, depression, and low self-esteem—all shown to be favorably affected by regular exercise.

Exercises like rope jumping decrease stress, probably through a combination of distraction (activity forces one to focus for a while on something other than the stress-causing situation), a burnoff of pent-up adrenalin, and possibly the release of endorphins—the body's natural painkillers and tranquilizers. Anxiety and depression are often the sidekicks of stress, so it stands to reason that they should part company together.

Rope jumping is also particularly well suited for improving one's self-esteem. In addition to its increasing one's fitness in all the areas discussed earlier in this chapter, the great variety of challenging yet achievable techniques ensures a recurring sense of accomplishment. Rope jumpers also get plenty of positive feedback from others. The current popular assumption is that rope jumping requires tremendous physical conditioning and coordination, and acknowledged rope jumpers automatically achieve athletic stature in the eyes of others. (As later chapters will show, however, with proper technique rope jumping is only modestly strenuous and is easily learned with a little guidance.) If verbal positive feedback isn't enough to raise one's self-esteem, then applause might do it. Great rope routines attract approving onlookers at any gym or health club. Show off a little, and you might be overwhelmed by calls for encores—just ask any of the AHA demonstration teams.

Accessible to Nearly Everyone

Another major strength of rope jumping is that it's unabashedly accessible to anyone—from kids on summer vacation to physical educators working with limited budgets. Here are a few words on each of rope jumping's user-friendly features:

• *Inexpensive.* The most costly item is a good pair of athletic shoes (about $40). The rest of the apparel is already hanging in the closet or locker. Jump ropes can be obtained very inexpensively from sport equipment catalogs, sporting goods stores, and direct mail order from manufacturers.

• *Not Dependent on Special Facilities or Weather Conditions.* All that's needed is enough room to swing the rope and a smooth, even floor to jump on—which gives lots of options, like the gymnasium when it's snowing, the outdoor basketball court when it's sunny, and so on.

• *Portable.* Some jump ropes can literally fit in a pocket with room for change—a real boon for those who travel frequently. For physical education and sport departments, there's no need to make an addition to the equipment room for the new order of ropes.

• *Safe.* Contrary to popular opinion, rope jumping is relatively easy on the knees. In fact, because rope jumping involves landing on the ball of the foot rather than on the heel, it has 1/2 to 1/7 the impact of running. Also, there is no danger of colliding into others, as in team sports, and there is less chance of twisting an ankle or knee from sudden, unexpected moves.

Offers Variety and Fun!

Of course, even the best exercise in blueprint is worthless if it doesn't generate smiles. In this regard, rope jumping is unsurpassed. Children all over the world spend entire recesses jumping rope to rhymes and games. For people of all age groups, jumping need never become boring, because there are literally hundreds of tempting techniques possible with a short rope alone. Add partner and long rope variations, and the possibilities soar into the

thousands. Some people also enjoy the challenges of speed or endurance jumping. For those who prefer to work out alone, it's nearly always possible to find a vacant room or gym corner. Those who thrive on comaraderie can gather other enthusiasts for a stimulating session.

Finally, and perhaps most importantly, rope jumping is a natural partner with music. Not only does a strong beat provide the tempos for turning the rope and moving the feet; the changing rhythms and melodies also give the impetus for varying techniques and styles. Rope jumpers can even aspire to becoming rope artists—dedicated enthusiasts who view the rope not as a piece of exercise equipment but as a versatile, expressive extension of themselves.

Summary

Few, if any, activities can measure up to the effectiveness, versatility, and accessibility of rope jumping. Its ability to develop nearly every major area of fitness makes it attractive for anyone in our harried society looking for an efficient all-around exercise and for coaches searching for that "cross-trainer" that will complement their training programs. Rope jumping's safety, inexpensiveness, and independence of weather conditions and special facilities means it won't put unnecessary demands on strapped physical education departments. Finally, students already familiar with rope jumping look forward to doing this exercise that is disguised as play. Those who have prejudices against the jump rope just might change their minds once the music is turned on and the ropes start spinning.

Is rope jumping the perfect exercise? Almost, but not quite. It does suffer from a few drawbacks that have especially deterred older individuals from partaking in the activity. Fortunately, there are simple solutions to these drawbacks, as the next chapter explains.

3
CHAPTER

Addressing the Complaints About Traditional Rope Jumping

With an Introduction to the Ropics® Program

By now, you might have formed the impression that rope jumping is a near-perfect exercise and blessed with immense potential. In fact, considering its array of advantages, it is perplexing that rope jumping has not achieved the horizons and opportunities of running, bicycling, or even newcomers like aerobic dance and triathlons. To be sure, groups like IRSO and AHA are making significant inroads, but major strides remain to be taken, especially in the postadolescent age groups.

Rope jumping's lack of popularity among older age groups can be traced to three drawbacks that are verified by popular experience, scientific research, or both. We must address these shortcomings because our goal is to prepare students for lifelong exercise, and because adult educators might not learn and teach rope jumping themselves unless it is made attractive for them. Let's briefly review the three complaints about traditional rope jumping and see how the unique Ropics program addresses them.

Complaint #1: Too Strenuous for Most Beginners

Children jump rope for the fun of it. When they become fatigued, it's no longer fun, so, they stop and rest until their seemingly boundless energy provokes them to go again. Older individuals usually exercise with slightly different motivations, however, and many become disturbed if they can't do a task for a reasonable length of time without undue exhaustion. Ask nearly any adult about rope jumping, and the first thing you will hear is, "I tried it, but it's too hard!"

Several scientific studies vindicate this complaint. Rope jumping is aerobically the same as running 9- to 10-minute miles or bicycling 13 miles per hour—too strenuous for exercise novices. To make matters worse, beginners work even harder and often stress their anaerobic metabolism because their muscles haven't yet learned how to jump rope efficiently. And unfortunately, the energy requirements don't decrease below the 9-to-10-minute-mile pace at slow jumping rates. In fact, the most efficient jumping rate is around 135 jumps per minute (a casual speed for single-time jumping).

Well-conditioned athletes, who can certainly handle the moderate aerobic requirements of basic rope jumping, also encounter problems. Because their legs often aren't accustomed to constantly jumping in place, shin splints and sore calves can become a real nuisance. In other words, these athletes can easily manage the cardiovascular demands of rope jumping but have trouble initially with the musculoskeletal demands.

Ropics' Solution #1: Gradually Increase Intensity by Introducing Low-Impact Techniques

Any healthy person can readily adapt to both the cardiovascular and the musculoskeletal demands of rope jumping if the intensity and duration of the sessions are *gradually* increased over time. Jumping slower does not decrease the intensity, so it is necessary to alternate traditional rope jumping with a less strenuous exercise. Children simply stop jumping when they're tired, and walk or stand. If they're using a long rope, they allow someone else to jump, or take turns spinning the rope, until they've rested. Adults could choose a similar strategy, but the Ropics program offers a more provocative option: *Alternate brief periods of conventional jumping techniques with periods of Low-Impact Techniques* (also known as Non-Jumping Techniques).

Low-Impact Techniques (LITs) form the corner-stone of Ropics and warrant some explanation. An LIT is any technique that does not require one to jump over the short rope (see, e.g., Figures 3.1a and b). Therefore, LITs require less energy and place little stress on the legs. At the same time, they allow the participant to continuously move and stay involved with the short rope rather than stopping and starting repeatedly with the despairing perception that rope jumping is just too tough. As participants become more fit and adept with the rope, they can increase the proportion of time spent jumping. Eventually, participants of nearly any age and fitness level can jump rope continuously for 15 minutes or more at a time without feeling uncomfortably winded or sore. Thus, LITs allow a gradual adaptation to the demands of rope jumping rather than forcing a certain level of fitness immediately—they operate, that is, on the "graduation principle."

LITs are rarely given up completely, however, because they add another dimension of fun and variety. Traditional programs offer hundreds of ways to jump over a rope; the LITs of the Ropics

| a | b |

Figure 3.1 An Open Step-Through (a) and a Waist Wrap (b)—examples of Low-Impact Techniques.

program add hundreds of ways to whirl, wrap, step through, and catch a rope. For advanced rope artists, LITs even make it easier to incorporate other disciplines such as dance, gymnastics, or the martial arts; rhythmic gymnastics, a growing women's Olympic sport, incorporates LITs into routines to just such an end.

Complaint #2: Difficult to Learn

"I'm too uncoordinated to jump rope," goes the second most common complaint. At first glance, this complaint seems justified also; after all, rope jumping requires a precise harmony of movement between the arms, legs, and rope. This appears to be a challenging task at least. However, one might also wonder why people don't share the same sentiment about swimming—another task that requires complex coordination between the upper and lower body. People who can only flail about in deep water will usually say it is because they were never taught to swim, not because they are too uncoordinated.

Ropics' Solution #2: Step-by-Step Instruction

Actually, most people have adequate coordination for mastering even advanced tricks. However, rope jumping is a skilled activity, just like swimming, and proper instruction is needed to develop the correct techniques and habits. Unfortunately, at times it seems that there is a conspiracy to show people wrong ways to jump rope. Many magazines, jump rope packages, and even some instructional books have used inexperienced models demonstrating improper form; one even showed a painfully grinning model jumping barefoot on a lawn with a rope that was too long.

The Jump Rope Primer uses only experienced jump rope enthusiasts to demonstrate techniques. Furthermore, in the Ropics program, techniques are broken down into their simplest components and taught step by step. For example, the reader will learn how to jump without the rope, how to hold the rope, how to turn the rope, and how to jump in time to the rope, before actually jumping over it (see pages 25-27). By using this approach, which is another extension of the graduation princi-

ple, even self-proclaimed klutzes have gone on to do public demonstrations of their finely honed skills.

Complaint #3: Lack of Stimulating Goals

The need to set and attain goals is a unique human trait. Even children, who often seem happy running around just to shed excess energy, quickly become goal oriented in their games. For example, running games like Tag, Hide-and-Seek, and Cops-and-Robbers have agreed-upon objectives. Likewise, children devise games in rope jumping where they must skip a certain number of times to a rhyme, or jump faster and faster or higher and higher until they miss. However, adolescents and adults usually aren't stimulated by these games, so different motivational strategies are needed for this age group.

Ropics' Solution #3: Progressive Technique Mastery

For rope jumping, the richest source of goals lies in the mastery of its many individual techniques. Mastering techniques at random, however, could be frustrating rather than motivating, because some are much more difficult than others or rely on earlier developed skills. Therefore, Ropics assigns a "difficulty factor" to each technique to provide both guidance and the short-term goal of learning a slightly more difficult technique. The Jump-Bounce and Windmills are the most basic techniques and have difficulty factors of 1.0. Quintuples, the most advanced (so far), has a difficulty factor of 5.8.

Ropics also divides the techniques into five separate skill levels (see Table 3.1). Techniques from Level 1 are the most basic and have difficulty factors of 1.0 to 1.9. Subsequent levels become more challenging; their techniques have difficulty factors with the first digit matching the skill-level number. Dividing techniques into levels is important motivationally because it gives the enthusiast a broader measuring stick—or a long-term goal akin to acquiring a more advanced belt in karate. Of course, difficulty factors and skill levels are also just one more example of the graduation principle—this

Table 3.1 Ropics Fundamental Organization of Short Rope Techniques

Skill level	Low-impact technique examples	Jumping technique examples
1 (Beginner) DF = 1.0-1.9	Windmill Figure-Eight	2-Foot Jump Bell
2 (Intermediate) DF = 2.0-2.9	Matador Whirl Forearm Wrap	Toe Touches Scissors
3 (Advanced Intermediate) DF = 3.0-3.9	180-Degree Figure-Eight	Matador Cross
4 (Advanced) DF = 4.0-4.9	Double Toss	Triples
5 (Master) DF = 5.0-5.9	Spin Kick Step-Through	Quadruples

time applied to learning a whole spectrum of techniques.

Summary

Rope jumping is blessed with many strengths, but it also has a few weaknesses that are especially important to the postadolescent age groups. The Ropics program gives at least one solution to each weakness: It decreases the aerobic and musculoskeletal demands by alternating brief periods of jumping with Low-Impact Techniques, it makes jump rope techniques easier to learn by teaching skills step by step, and it provides motivating goals through mastery of progressively more challenging techniques. Now even more people can consider rope jumping an attractive exercise alternative and take advantage of its tremendous benefits.

4
CHAPTER

Learning the Ropes and Other Information

As we've seen in the preceding chapters, rope jumping provides many exercise benefits, and its few drawbacks are easily overcome with the Ropics program. To maximize those benefits, it is essential to use the right shoes, jump ropes, and floor surfaces—and even the right music.

Jump Ropes

Jump ropes are obviously central, and choosing the right one can mean the difference between disappointment and enjoyment. Their apparent simplicity is deceptive. A rope's performance can be affected by such qualities as aerodynamic drag, weight, length, durability, and how well it turns.

Figure 4.1

How to Measure a Jump Rope

Getting the right length rope for singles rope jumping is important. Ropes that are too short lead to bad jumping posture and frequent misses, especially with fancy techniques. Ropes that are too long strike the floor in front of the feet and bounce up to hit the ankles.

To measure a rope, one should stand on its midpoint with one foot. The end of the handles should just reach the armpits, as in Figure 4.1. Some participants, especially beginners, prefer a slightly longer rope; they should measure the rope with *both* feet on the middle of the rope. A perfect fit is not necessary for noncompetitors, and a mix of different lengths of ropes as listed below will satisfy most classes. If a participant wants a custom fit,

adjust the rope per the instructions of that particular brand or style. If the rope is not adjustable, and it is too long, tie knots in the rope several inches from the handles as needed. If a rope requires more than four knots, it's best to get a shorter one.

Here are the most common jump rope lengths for different grades (a few shorter and a few longer ropes should be available for most classes):

- Kindergarten to grade 2: 7 ft
- Grades 3 through 5: 8 ft
- Grades 6 through 12: 9 ft

Ropes used for long rope and Double Dutch routines are typically 14 to 16 ft long and do not need to be adjusted for different heights. If a specific jumper is taller than the average, the turners simply take a slight step toward each other to make the loop larger.

How to Choose a Jump Rope

The National Sporting Goods Association estimates that $13 million worth of jump ropes were sold in 1989 alone, including jump ropes of every brand, design, and material on the market today. Here are general guidelines that are helpful in selecting a jump rope:

- Look for ropes that are well constructed and made of durable materials. Children and playgrounds are especially tough on ropes, so be wary of "bargains" that might not make it through one recess.
- The rope should turn easily within the handle, but bearings are not always necessary—speed and segmented ropes turn well even without this wear-prone and somewhat expensive part.
- Avoid ropes that stretch significantly when you pull a section between your hands. "Elastic" jump ropes are unwieldy, especially at faster speeds.
- The handles should fit comfortably in the hands. Smaller individuals may find some handles too large to be comfortable for extended periods of time. Those who tend to get sweaty palms should try handles with foam rubber grips.

The following are the major types of jump ropes, each with its own particular strengths and weaknesses. (The price ranges listed are for bulk purchases of short ropes. Long ropes and small orders cost more.)

SPEED ROPES (A.K.A. "LICORICE ROPES")

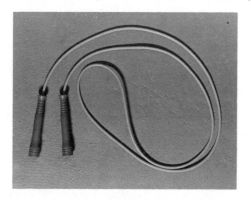

Figure 4.2 Rope by Ex-U-Rope, Inc.

Aptly named, speed ropes ($1.50-$3.50) are made from vinyl plastic cords that resemble licorice candy, their other namesake. These ropes are favored by jump rope demonstration teams and competitors because they are light, cut the air easily, and consequently are fast. They are also the most favored by schools and organizations because they are probably the most durable and yet among the least expensive. They also work well as long ropes for Double Dutch and other variations.

Unfortunately, speed ropes are not ideal for several Low-Impact Techniques in the Ropics program because they tend to become gnarled. It is also easier to miss with these ropes because their light weight makes them less forgiving to slight errors. Many brands are also difficult to adjust for different heights, although they can be ordered in different lengths, or knots can be tied in them. Despite these drawbacks, speed ropes remain the number one choice for most schools and institutions.

SEGMENTED ROPES (A.K.A. "BEADED ROPES")

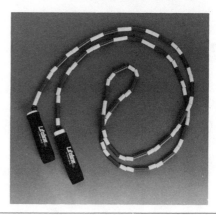

Figure 4.3 Rope by Lifeline International, Inc.

Segmented ropes ($1.75-$4.00) have one-and-one-half-inch-long cylindrical plastic beads strung on an inner nylon cord. These ropes are slightly heavier than most other ropes, and are therefore more forgiving to slight errors in execution, and they handle the wind better for outdoor rope jumping. They are the ropes best suited for the Low-Impact Techniques unique to Ropics. Additionally, by simply undoing the knot at the end of the nylon cord and removing the appropriate number of beads, one can easily shorten one of these ropes to fit even the youngest skipper. If the rope is too short, a longer nylon cord can be purchased from a hardware store and the beads from the original rope restrung onto the longer one. Of course, longer ropes can sometimes be requested directly from the manufacturer.

The biggest disadvantage to a segmented rope is that it has the greatest sting if it strikes the participant during a miss. These are also the noisiest ropes if you teach class on wood floors. In some quarters, segmented ropes have acquired ill repute for breaking on impact with hard surfaces. This is a fault only of inexpensive, usually imported, ropes that use cheap, brittle beads. Quality segmented ropes are nearly as durable as speed ropes.

COTTON ROPES

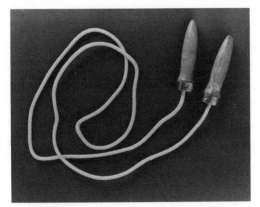

Figure 4.4

Ropes made of natural fibers, like cotton ($1.50-$3.00), predate all others, and yet they still hold their own on retail shelves. Their principal advantage is that they don't sting if the rope accidentally slaps the participant, so they are ideal for surviving the repeated misses that are inevitable when learning difficult techniques. In fact, a number nine sash cord from the hardware store is an inexpensive rope for just such circumstances. If you plan to use a cotton rope as your primary rope, however, purchase one that turns on ball bearings for smoother turning. Another advantage to cotton ropes, which may be especially appreciated with large classes, is that they don't make much noise when they strike a hard floor.

The principle disadvantage of cotton ropes is that they are the slowest type because the fibers generate drag at higher rope-turning speeds. They also tend to become gnarled with some Low-Impact Techniques and handle poorly in the wind.

SYNTHETIC FIBER ROPES

Figure 4.5

Ropes made from materials like nylon and polypropylene ($1.50-$3.00) share many of the characteristics of cotton ropes. Because the fibers are denser, though, they are slightly faster than cotton ropes. The trade-off is that they also sting a little more. Polypropylene also has the annoying trait of fraying as it wears, which slows it down and causes it to catch on carpets. There doesn't seem to be a definite niche for these ropes outside of rhythmic gymnastics, where they have the right balance of characteristics for their style.

LEATHER ROPES

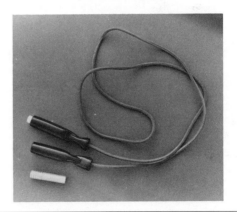

Figure 4.6   Rope by Ex-U-Rope, Inc.

The classic leather jump rope ($5.00-$15.00) made popular by generations of boxers can be viewed as the organic version of speed ropes and shares their handling characteristics. They have been associated with athletes for so long, while the other ropes were found mainly on playgrounds, that many people still consider them the only serious jump rope on the market. Consequently, leather ropes are still popular in sporting goods stores. They can't be found in many schools or even in the hands of most jump rope competitors, though, because they are more expensive, less durable, and a bit slower than the plastic version.

WEIGHTED ROPES

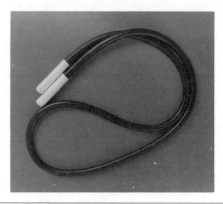

Figure 4.7   Rope by Body Flex, Inc.

As we discussed in chapter 2, rope jumping is good for toning the upper extremities. Wouldn't it be great if one could develop significantly greater upper body strength while reaping all the other benefits of the rope simultaneously? That is the intent of the various jump rope designs that add weight to either the handles or the rope itself ($10.00-$30.00). Whether such ropes succeed in building greater strength is a question that remains unanswered by controlled studies.

We have reservations about any design that adds more than 1/2 pound to a 9-foot rope. (Some models can weigh up to 6 pounds.) Heavily weighted ropes like the one in Figure 4.7 make rope jumping extremely taxing for even well-conditioned athletes. These massive ropes, which are made of solid rubber or sand-filled latex tubes, require not only slow, ponderous turns, but also higher jumps to maintain the rhythm. Overuse injuries might become a problem, especially for children, because the relatively small muscles and tendons of the upper extremities could be overstressed by the torque generated. And most upper extremity contractions during basic rope jumping are isometric, which would develop strength through only a limited range of motion.

Weighted jump ropes weighing less than 1/2 pound, or having small weights in the handle as in

Figure 4.6, may have merit for experienced athletic rope jumpers. In sport, power, which is a product of speed and strength, is often an important attribute. The more modestly weighted ropes would allow turning the rope faster to develop power while maintaining good rope jumping form.

Facilities

Gymnasiums, racquetball or tennis courts, pool decks, dance studios, outdoor rubberized running tracks, a vacant corner in the weight room, and nearly any large room are all possible places to swing the rope. Each rope jumper will require about an 8-foot-by-8-foot unobstructed area and a 9-foot or higher ceiling (children slightly less). Long rope routines typically require at least a 20-foot-by-20-foot area and at least a 10-foot ceiling.

Floor Surfaces

As the aerobic dance industry has learned, flooring can have a large affect on leg injury. A number of companies have spent considerable resources to develop and market the ideal flooring for athletes and exercise enthusiasts. In rope jumping, the floor can also affect how often the participant misses the rope.

The "suspended" wood flooring found in many dance and exercise studios is ideal for rope jumping because the floor flexes to absorb impact, returns the energy back for rebound, and provides a stable platform. Solid wood, rubber-tiled, and polyurethane floors are also acceptable. A carpet with a low nap and modest amount of padding would be a third choice.

Thick-napped or thick-padded carpets are not well suited for rope jumping. Much like when running in sand, feet tend to sink into this surface and lose the spring needed for the next rebound. Not only is the work harder—timing suffers, which increases the frequency of misses. If a student wishes to jump at home on the carpet, suggest that he or she place a vinyl chair mat over the carpet. The chair mat should have cleats on the underside to prevent it from slipping. This creates a more stable surface that still flexes a bit.

Asphalt has some "give" to it on warm days, but its rough surface wears out the middle of ropes rather quickly. Concrete and hard-tiled floors should be avoided, if possible, because these unforgiving surfaces increase the risk of shin splints, sore calves, and other leg and foot injuries. If your exercise area has such a floor, good athletic shoes (discussed next) become even more important. Also, *Sportime*, a sport equipment catalog, offers cushioned mats specially designed for rope jumping. Call 404-449-5700 for more information.

Recommended Apparel

The shoe requirements for rope jumping are similar to those for aerobic dance: good forefoot cushioning and lateral support. It's no surprise, then, that comfortable, well-fitted, quality aerobic dance shoes are best suited for rope jumping. Certain cross-training shoes now in vogue also work well. Regardless of brand or style, the student should give shoes a test jump in the store (without the rope is fine!) before purchasing them.

Of course, most students won't run out and buy the optimal rope jumping shoe, but be aware of the drawbacks of other types of shoes. Court shoes designed for basketball or tennis have good lateral support, but modest forefoot cushioning. (If you can, get students to lace up their shoes snugly—explain that ankle sprains and limping are even more out of fashion than laced basketball shoes.) Running shoes usually have decent forefoot cushioning, but they universally lack the lateral support needed for many footwork techniques. Styles with knobby soles tend to snag the rope as it passes under the feet. Of course, dress or casual shoes often aren't even made for walking, much less for jumping. Finally, rope jumping isn't kind to those who prefer to jump unshod, because a rope striking naked toes smarts.

The outfit should be rounded out with comfortable athletic wear that doesn't restrict movement or prevent sweat from wicking away from the body. For support, mature women will want to wear a leotard or an athletic bra or both. Participants with long hairstyles will want to use barrettes or bands to keep their hair out of their eyes. Men should wear snug briefs or an athletic supporter. Wrist and head bands are appreciated by those who sweat profusely.

Music for Rope Jumping

Music and jump ropes are inseparable partners. Not only does music provide the impetus to get the feet jumping and the rope(s) spinning, but the varying rhythms and melodies make it challenging and fun to try to match techniques and speed. Group routines choreographed to music can be exciting for participants and spectators alike. Because rope jumping is relatively stationary, any music system, including a portable radio or cassette player, can provide accompaniment.

The choice of music depends on your students' or your own tastes. Pop, rock, polka, swing, rap, country and western, and jazz are just some of the options. For beginning to intermediate students, it is especially helpful to have music with 120 to 140 beats per minute because this is the most efficient jumping rate. As students become more advanced, music with more complicated beats and rhythms can be used to challenge their timing and agility.

Summary

Having the right equipment, apparel, and facilities are important for getting the most out of rope jumping. For most schools, speed ropes are the jump ropes of choice due to their inexpensiveness and durability. For safety, the proper shoes and the right floor surface are the most important considerations because rope jumping does involve repetitive, albeit modest, impact. Finally, to increase the fun of rope jumping about tenfold, be sure to round up music that practically makes the ropes turn by themselves.

II PART
Illustrated Jump Rope Techniques

Literally thousands of techniques are possible with jump ropes, and with proper instruction and a little practice, nearly anyone can master an impressive number of them. The next two chapters present common or intriguing techniques that give students a good sample of what's possible with both short and long ropes. They also give students a solid foundation of skills needed for jump rope games and events and for developing even further skills with the rope.

5
CHAPTER

Short Rope Techniques

The short jump rope appeals to people of all ages and is therefore the most important jump rope variation to learn in anticipation of lifelong exercise. Because the participant turns the rope as well as jumps over it (in most situations), it also conditions more areas of the body than the long rope.

General Tips for Teaching or Learning Techniques

Every technique poses its own challenges. Nevertheless, the following tips will facilitate the mastery of almost every short rope technique.

Tips for Teaching Short Rope Techniques

• **When possible, teach the technique step by step.** For example, with the Jogging Step, first show the footwork without the rope. Next, have students turn their ropes at their sides while lightly jogging in place to get a feel for the timing. Then, when everyone is ready, do the actual technique. Variations on this approach will work for most techniques. For instance, with Front Crosses, have them practice crossing their arms without worrying about jumping over the rope, as a first step. The second step would be to jump over the rope just once before advancing to repetitive Front Crosses.

• **Have inexperienced students turn the rope only in a forward direction.** The rope should approach the toes before the heels as in Figure 5.1. Turning the rope in the opposite direction, or backward, is more difficult for most participants and poses a small safety risk because the rope can fly to the face during a miss.

• **Let one of your more experienced students instruct the others.** This is especially helpful if you have trouble demonstrating a technique. Children often learn quickly, even from pictures, because they haven't developed many of the inhibitions that burden us more "mature" people. Just be sure the student demonstrates the technique at a moderate speed.

• **Teach only two to four new techniques with each class.** Attempting to teach and learn too many new skills at once can be frustrating.

• **Teach at least one new Low-Impact Technique with each class.** This gives the students something to work on when they become fatigued from jumping.

• **Teach basic techniques before teaching the more advanced ones.** To help you out with this principle and improve your students' motivation, we have assigned a difficulty factor (DF) to each technique, as discussed on page 13.

Figure 5.1

In making difficulty factor assignments we weighed how much the technique required from the following areas in order to be executed successfully:

- Coordination/agility
- Strength
- Timing
- Rhythmic skill
- Flexibility

Of, course, the DF is only meant as a general guide. Turning the rope with the nondominant hand or in the backward direction can significantly increase the difficulty. Also, a technique that is challenging to one participant may be quite easy for another, depending on the student's individual talents or stage of motor skill development. For example, a Windmill is the easiest technique to learn for most older children and adults and has a DF of 1.0. Young children, however, often find it more difficult to make the rope turn smoothly on one side than to jump over the rope.

Naming a technique can be almost as challenging as assigning a DF. At present, no nomenclature committee exists to standardize names for techniques. Consequently, most techniques have several names depending on which book you read, what organization you belong to, or what area of the country you live in—a seemingly trivial matter until enthusiasts try to communicate with each other. In naming techniques for *The Primer*, we attempted to use names that are concise and descriptive and have a minimum of prepositions. The last consideration becomes important when you run up against names like *Backward Front-Back Crossover*. Considerable weight was also given to names already in use by AHA and IRSO, because their nomenclature is most widespread.

You'll remember from chapter 3 that the Ropics program divides its techniques into five levels, with difficulty factors ranging from 1.0 to 5.8. The techniques we describe in *The Jump Rope Primer* cover only the first three levels: beginning, intermediate, and advanced intermediate. As you prepare to learn the techniques and to teach them to your students, you should note the technique's level, name, and difficulty factor.

Level 1 (Beginning) Techniques

Level 1 techniques are the easiest to master but are also the most important, because all later techniques build upon the foundation of skills and habits acquired here. This stage is also critical for inspiring confidence in students about their rope jumping abilities.

Learning the Basic Jump-Bounce (DF = 1.0) and Two-Foot Jump (DF = 1.2)

STEP 1

Figure 5.2

Step 1 is learning how to jump properly without the rope. While the students are in the chosen formation, have them lay their ropes out straight and stand next to the ropes with feet together. Using the verbal cue "One-two-ready-jump," have them jump over their ropes once as in Figure 5.2. Repeat several times while reminding the class to keep feet together and jump just high enough to clear the rope.

STEP 2

Figure 5.3

Step 2 is learning to jump rhythmically over the stationary rope. There are two basic rhythms children use most frequently with rope jumping. The first is "half-time" or "jump-bouncing." To teach this rhythm, have the students jump over the stationary rope, make a rebound, and then jump over the rope again to repeat the sequence on each side. Use the verbal cue "Jump, bounce, jump, bounce, jump . . . ." If some students are having difficulty, hold their hands and jump over their ropes with them as illustrated in Figure 5.3.

The second rhythm is "single-time" jumping, in which a single jump is made to each turn of the rope. Use the verbal cue "Jump, jump, jump. . . ."

STEP 3

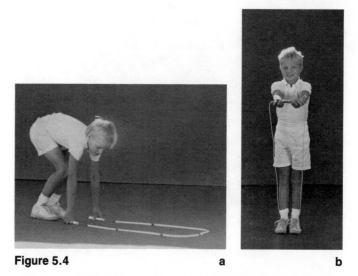

Figure 5.4   a   b

Step 3 is learning how to hold the rope properly. Instruct the students to place the ends of the rope handles at their toes. When they bend over to pick up their ropes, as shown in Figure 5.4a, they will have automatically grasped them correctly. To verify that they indeed do have the ropes held properly, tell them to "tap, tap" the ends together, as in Figure 5.4b.

STEP 4

Figure 5.5

In ***Step 4*** the students learn how to turn the rope. Have them place the middle of the rope at their achilles tendon. With the arms extended downward and in front of the body, tell them to "tug, tug" (pull forward on the handles), as in Figure 5.5. Next have the students swing their ropes overhead with their wrists and forearms. Use the verbal cue sequence "Tug, tug—circle." (Stop them from *throwing* their ropes up over their heads.) Do not allow students to jump over their ropes at first. Have them step over them and repeat the "tug, tug—circle" sequence several times.

STEP 5

Step 5 finally gets to the real thing—actual rope jumping. When the students have mastered steps 1 through 4, have them jump over their ropes just once rather than step over them. Repeat the series of skills learned in step 4, and use the entire verbal cue sequence "Tug, tug—circle—jump." (Students who lose an end of the rope should start over from step 3 and add "tap, tap" to the beginning of the cue sequence.) As they practice jumping, tell them to concentrate on three things:

- Turning the rope with the wrists and forearms, not the entire arm (don't make big circles)
- Keeping the feet together and not kicking back
- Jumping just high enough to clear the rope (1/2 to 1 inch)

You might have a contest to see who can jump the softest and with the smallest arm circles.

STEP 6

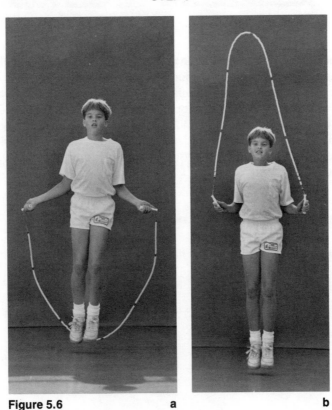

Figure 5.6   a   b

When they can confidently jump over the rope once, it's time for *Step 6*, rhythmic jumping. Many children are accustomed to half-time jumping as shown in Figures 5.6a and b (Jump-Bounce). With this rhythm, a jump occurs when the rope is underneath the *feet and* when the rope is overhead. You can use the verbal cue sequence "Tug, tug—circle—jump, bounce, jump, bounce. . . ." Note again that the rope is turned from the wrists and forearms.

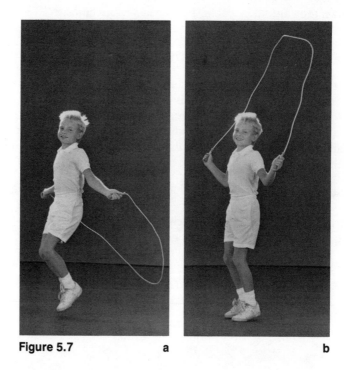

Figure 5.7   a   b

More experienced jumpers prefer the single-time rhythm, in which a single jump is made for each turn of the rope (with no rebound in between) as in Figures 5.7a and b (Two-Foot Jump). The rope must turn faster during single time. Use the verbal cue ". . . jump, jump, jump. . . ." Again, the rope is turned from the wrists and forearms, the feet are kept together, and the jump is just high enough to clear the rope.

The hard part is over when your students have learned how to do basic rope jumping properly. The following pages depict just a few of the thousands of other possible jump rope techniques.

More Level 1 Rope Jumping Techniques

(All techniques are illustrated in single-time rhythm)

SKIER (DF = 1.3)

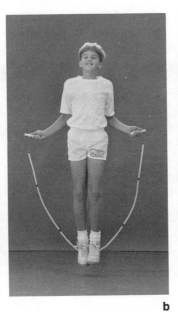

Figure 5.8   a   b   c

As in downhill skiing, the jump is about 1/2 foot from side to side while keeping the feet together. Note that the rope makes it around without catching the toes because the feet are directly underneath the body when the rope passes under. This is the case for most footwork variations.

TWIST (DF = 1.4)

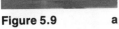

Figure 5.9   a   b   c   d

As the name implies, the feet are kept together while the jumper twists at the waist from side to side. Beginners may want to twist only halfway with each turn of the rope. Get out the Chubby Checker record!

BELL (DF = 1.5)

Figure 5.10   a   b   c   d

The feet are kept together, and the student jumps about 1/2 foot forward and then backward. This technique is not difficult to learn but does require more energy. Remember, practice the footwork without the rope first.

RUN STEP (DF = 1.7)

Figure 5.11   a   b   c   d

As when running, the heels are alternately kicked back with each turn of the rope. Avoid teaching beginners this technique until they have mastered the more basic and efficient techniques. Kicking the heels back should be an optional technique rather than a habit, because it requires more energy.

JOGGING STEP (DF = 1.8)

Figure 5.12   **a**   **b**   **c**   **d**

As when lightly jogging, the student lightly pushes off alternating feet with each turn of the rope. This takes a little more practice to master than the Two-Foot Jump, as the DF indicates, but it is well worth the trouble because it is the most efficient way to jump rope.

Level 1 Low-Impact Techniques

WINDMILLS (DF = 1.0)

Figure 5.13   **a**   **b**   **c**

The rope is turned in a circle at one side, at first with the dominant hand and in a forward direction, as in Figure 5.13a. The student should concentrate on turning the rope smoothly from the wrist and forearm rather than from the shoulder.

There are many Windmill variations, because the rope can be turned on any side (right, left, front, back, overhead), in two rotational directions, and with either or both hands. Figure 5.13b illustrates a two-handed Front Windmill, and Figure 5.13c shows a one-handed Overhead Windmill (a.k.a. "Helicopter").

FIGURE-EIGHTS (DF = 1.3)

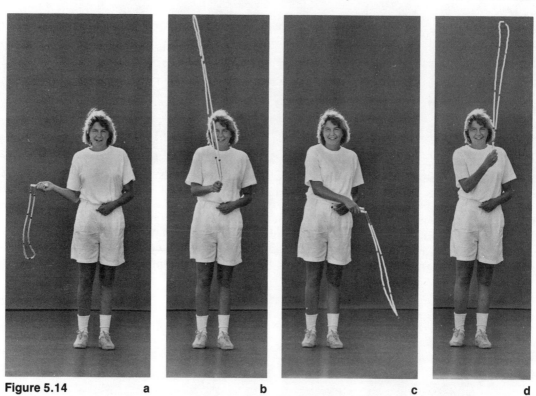

Figure 5.14   a   b   c   d

The student turns the rope at one side and alternately changes sides as the rope comes forward. The rope travels in a figure-eight pattern. Again, have the student practice with the rope turning in a forward direction first. Figure-Eights can be done with both hands as well. Two-handed Figure Eights are often used for transitions between techniques and as a prelude to jumping; parting the hands allows one to begin jumping because the rope is already up to speed.

SWING WRAP (DF = 1.4)

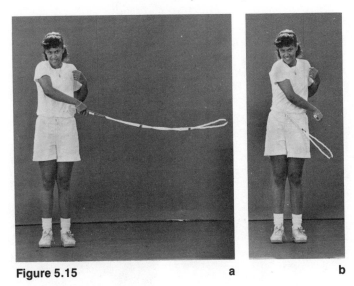

Figure 5.15   a   b

Have the student begin with a one-handed Overhead Windmill using the dominant hand. As the rope comes forward, the hand is brought down to waist level so the rope lightly wraps around the waist. The rope is pulled back to reverse the rotation for another Overhead Windmill, or the student can go into an entirely different technique. Wraps are one of several methods for reversing rope rotation.

FOOT CATCH (DF = 1.4)

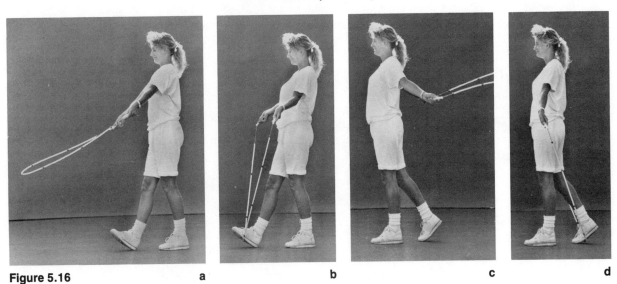

Figure 5.16   a   b   c   d

As the first two photos show, when the rope is turning forward the middle of the rope is caught by lifting the toes as the rope comes under. The heel is lifted, as in the last two photos, if the rope is turning backward. This technique is a snappy way to end a routine or to stop the rope for reversing direction.

LEG OVER PASS (DF = 1.7)

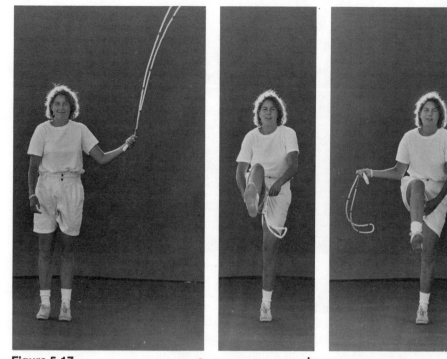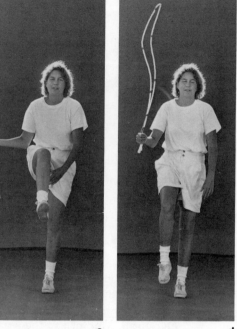

Figure 5.17　　　　　a　　　　　　　b　　　　　　　c　　　　　　　d

In preparation for the Leg Over Pass, the student should be certain that he or she can pass the rope ends from hand to hand while doing Figure-Eights. When ready, the student continues the Figure-Eights but passes the rope under the opposite lifted leg to the other hand. Of course, the rope may be passed in the other direction also.

Level 2 (Intermediate) Techniques

Now that the basics have been learned and confidence has been increased, it's time to begin learning more advanced techniques. Also encourage the students to create variations of their own.

Representative Level 2 Rope Jumping Techniques

SIDE STRADDLE (DF = 2.0)

Figure 5.18   a   b   c   d

Also known as "Jumping Jacks," Side Straddles are easily learned once the timing is understood. The feet must be coming together or just beginning to spread apart when the rope passes underneath the body. The feet are in contact with the ground, either spread apart or close together, when the rope is overhead. Stress again that the jumps should be light and easy. Some students initially jump high and throw their legs out quickly. As with most jumping techniques, you should barely hear the feet landing on the floor.

SCISSORS (DF = 2.1)

Figure 5.19   a   b

The Scissors is much like the action of cross-country skiing. On the first jump, one leg is split forward and the other leg backward. On the next jump the legs reverse positions.

FRONT STRADDLE (DF = 2.2)

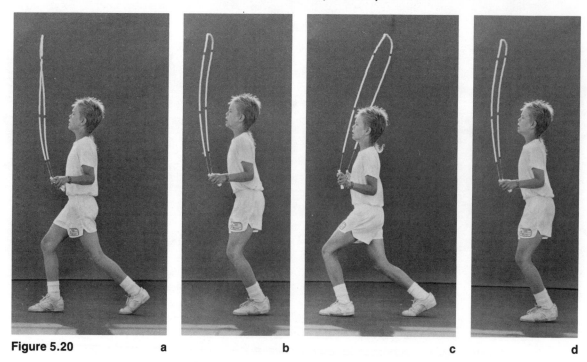

Figure 5.20   a   b   c   d

The Front Straddle is like the Scissors except that the legs do not reverse the split with each jump. Instead, the feet are brought together between splits.

TOE TOUCHES/HEEL TOUCHES (DF = 2.4/2.3)

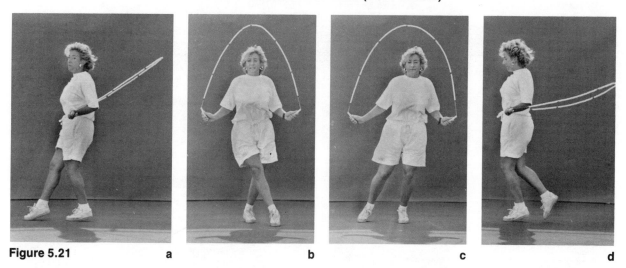

Figure 5.21   a   b   c   d

e f g

The toe or heel of either foot can be touched to the floor on the front, side, or across the other leg. Toe touches can also be done to the back. Remember, the touches to the various sides are completed when the rope is overhead. Toe Touches are a little harder than Heel Touches because the rope snags an extended foot more readily than a flexed foot.

This is an excellent technique for allowing the students to practice creating their own sequences, because so many touch combinations exist. Some examples:

Heel to front, (jump) toe to back, repeat.

Toe to front, (jump) toe to side, (jump) toe to back, (jump) change foot and repeat pattern.

KNEE LIFTS/HIGH STEP (DF = 2.6/2.8)

Figure 5.22   a   b   c   d

The knees are lifted alternately with every other turn of the rope. This technique really works the hip flexors. A particularly demanding variation, High Steps, requires the participant to lift alternate knees with *every* turn of the rope, much like running in place through tires.

CROSS STEP (DF = 2.6)

Figure 5.23   a   b   c   d

Instead of just bringing the feet together as during Side Straddles, the student crosses one leg behind the other. On the next turn, the legs are split to a straddle position and then crossed again, but with the opposite leg in front. This technique requires a little more agility.

FRONT CROSS (DF = 2.9)

Figure 5.24   a   b   c   d

Have students begin by first learning the arm movement without being concerned about jumping over the rope. The rope is placed at the heels and then swung overhead. As the rope approaches its zenith, the student begins to cross the arms so that they overlap at mid forearm by the time the rope is at the toes. Beginners may find it helpful to exaggerate the arm cross by "gluing their elbows together." Repeat until the action is smooth and it seems that the rope would pass under the feet if the student would jump.

Common mistakes are to have the arms crossed unequally or to have the handles drooping down rather than pointing out to the sides.

When the first step is mastered, have the students jump over the rope just once, keeping the above points in mind. The student should begin to uncross the arms when the rope is overhead again and continue with standard jumping. As experience and confidence is gained, the arms can be continuously crossed and uncrossed. Students can motivate themselves by setting a goal of doing just one more front cross with each attempt or practice session. Another challenging variation is to keep the arms constantly crossed while jumping.

Representative Level 2 Low-Impact Techniques

FOREARM WRAP (DF = 2.0)

Figure 5.25   a   b   c   d

The rope is turned at the right side with both hands. The right arm is extended, and the rope wraps around it. The rope will wrap wherever the left hand is placed, so it should be placed near the right mid-forearm to facilitate control. To unwrap, the arm rotation is reversed when the wrap is complete. As with all Wrap techniques, the rope turns in the opposite direction after completion.

A more interesting option for unwrapping the rope is to bring the right arm across the chest to the left side at any point during the Wrap. Now the rope will unwind using the momentum already generated. Of course, Forearm Wraps can be done to both sides.

UPPER ARM WRAP (DF = 2.3)

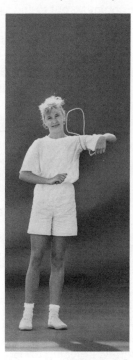

Figure 5.26 a b c d

As with the Forearm Wrap, the rope is swung to the side and one arm is extended. Now, however, the wrist of the extended arm is *flexed* so that the rope wraps on the same upper arm. The free hand pulls and reverses the rotation to unwind the rope. This technique works better with speed ropes than with segmented ropes because the beads tend to catch the skin.

MATADOR WHIRL (DF = 2.4)

Figure 5.27 a b c

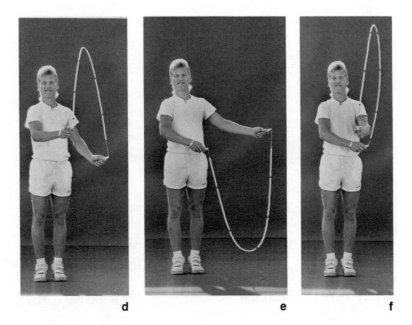

d   e   f

This is a difficult technique to explain and illustrate because it closely resembles Figure-Eights. The difference is that the arms "roll" over each other on each side so that the rope makes two circles before switching to the right or left. Matador Whirls have a very natural feel to them when mastered and often replace Figure-Eights as a transition technique with advanced rope jumpers.

SAMURAI WHIRL (DF = 2.6)

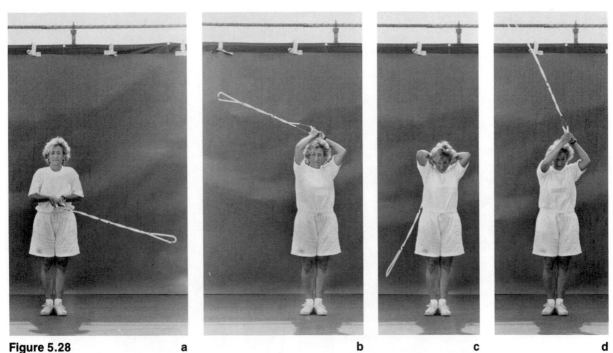

Figure 5.28   a   b   c   d

The Samurai is essentially a Figure-Eight done from the front to back rather than from side to side. The student begins by doing Front Windmills in the counterclockwise direction. As the rope begins its ascent, the hands are brought over and behind the head so the rope makes one turn in that position. As the rope makes its ascent again, the hands are brought back in front to complete the cycle. A Samurai can also be done with only one hand holding both ends of the rope.

WAIST WRAP (DF = 2.7)

Figure 5.29　　　　　a　　　　　　　　　　b　　　　　　　　　　c　　　　　　　　　　d

This technique begins with Overhead Windmills to the right with two hands. As the rope comes forward, the left hand is brought down behind the back while the right hand circles to bring the remaining rope overhead. Just as the rope comes around the second time, the right hand is brought down to waist level to complete the wrap. To unwrap, the right hand is lifted overhead again and unwinds the rope.

Waist Wraps are often more difficult for experienced rope jumpers to master than for novices because two habits must be broken: (a) The rope must turn horizontally rather than vertically, and (b) the arms must move independently rather then mirroring each other. Once mastered, Waist Wraps can be initiated directly from other techniques without the preliminary Overhead Windmill. Learning these skills is one of the prerequisites to learning how to finely manipulate a jump rope.

OPEN STEP-THROUGH (DF = 2.7)

Figure 5.30　　　　　a　　　　　　　　　　b　　　　　　　　　　c　　　　　　　　　　d

As the name implies, one leg steps through the rope at a time. The student begins by turning the rope forward with both hands to the right. As the rope comes down, the student places the right hand between the legs and brings the left hand over the head to turn the rope, lifting each leg as the rope approaches it.

The secret to mastering Step-Throughs is being able to turn the upper half of the rope in a horizontal direction rather than vertically as in jumping. Students often learn this technique more easily by initiating it with a Waist Wrap. Then, as the rope unwinds, one simply continues turning the hand overhead and places the other hand between the legs. Once truly mastered, however, Open Step-Throughs can be approached directly from Figure-Eights and even from a jumping technique.

Three Examples of Level 3 (Advanced Intermediate) Techniques

Now we are getting into the "wow" techniques. Although Level 3 is more advanced, most students can still learn these techniques with a little practice and perseverance.

MATADOR CROSS (DF = 3.2)

Figure 5.31   a   b   c   d

Also known as the "Side-Swing Cross," this technique could be viewed as a Side Windmill into a Front Cross. Have students begin by learning just the arm movement. The student swings the rope to the left side with both hands and as the rope approaches its zenith, crosses the left arm over the right (the right hand stays at the left side) to bring the rope down to the feet.

When the action is smooth and the rope approaches the feet, the student jumps over the rope and begins to uncross the arms when it is overhead. After the jump, both hands may be brought to either side again to repeat the process.

180-DEGREE TURN-ABOUT
(FRONT TO BACK: DF = 3.0; BACK TO FRONT: DF = 3.2)

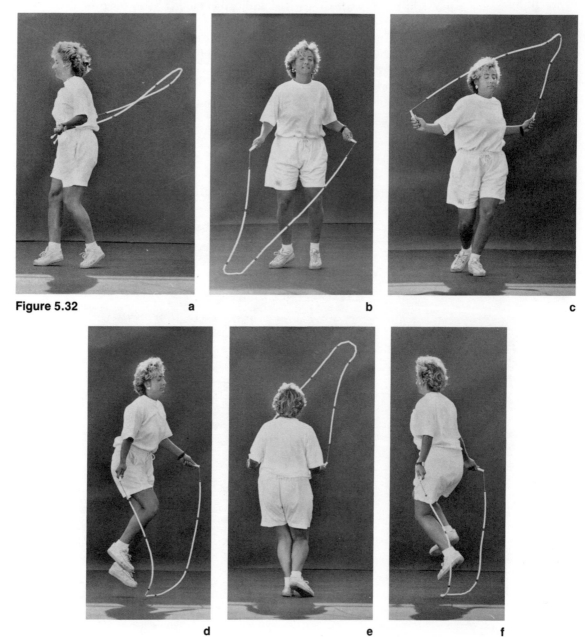

Figure 5.32   a   b   c

          d   e   f

(Before they learn Turn-Abouts, students should be adept at jumping with the rope turning backward.)

While turning the rope forward, the student brings it over to the left side and pivots the body 180 degrees toward that side as the rope comes down. By the time the rope is overhead, the student should be facing the opposite direction. The rope should now be turning backward and come around to meet the heels. Again, students shouldn't worry about jumping over the rope at first.

When the movement feels comfortable, the student jumps over the rope just after pivoting. When the 180-Degree Turn-About is completed, the student will be jumping backward. One can return to original position by swinging the rope to the other side and then pivoting the body 180 degrees to jump forward again. When both directions are mastered, students can jump continuously while turning in a circle! The 180-Degree Turn-About is one of those keystone techniques that open a world of new possibilities.

180-DEGREE FIGURE-EIGHT (DF = 3.0)

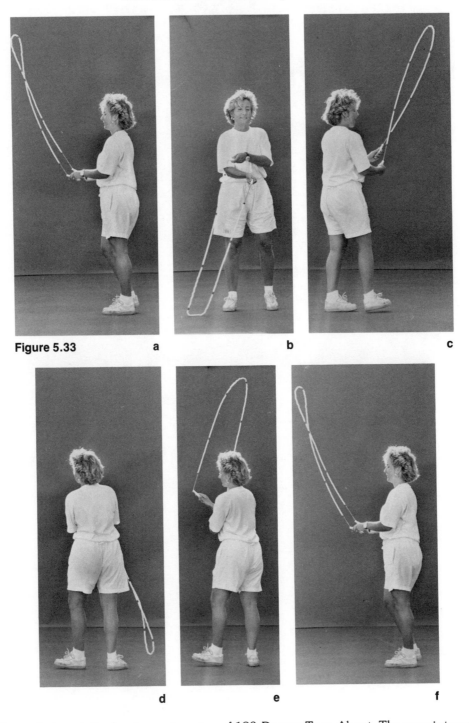

Figure 5.33   a   b   c

d   e   f

This technique is the low-impact version of 180-Degree Turn-About. The rope is turned in a forward direction on the left side. The body pivots 180 degrees to the left as the rope comes down. After the body turns, the rope will be on the right side again, though turning backward. Both hands are brought across the waist to bring rope over the left side again, and the body pivots 180 degrees in that direction. The rope will now be at the right side and turning forward again. Of course, 180-Degree Figure-Eights can also be done by turning to the right.

6
CHAPTER

Long Rope Techniques

The 14- to 16-foot "long rope" is popular among preteens and complements the short rope because it adds the dimension of teamwork. The techniques and variations are also just as numerous, challenging, and fun to do and watch. It may appear that only a few long rope techniques are taught in *The Jump Rope Primer*. Keep in mind, however, that all the footwork variations taught with the short rope can be done while jumping over the long rope. Also, children will readily create variations on their own if they understand the basics and are offered a few imaginative ideas to start out with.

Single Long Rope Techniques

SINGLE LONG ROPE TURNING SKILLS (DF = 1.0)

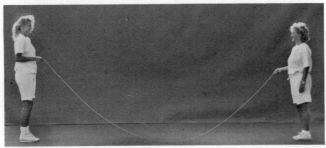

Figure 6.1   a

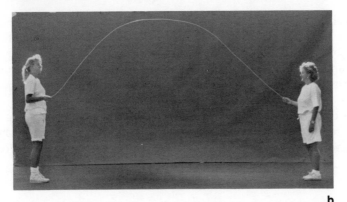

b

To turn the long rope, the upper arm remains stationary while the forearm rotates. The wrist stays locked with the thumb on top of the handle. The middle of the rope should just touch the ground.

BASIC JUMPING WITH THE SINGLE LONG ROPE (JUMP-BOUNCE) (DF = 1.0)

Figure 6.2

The novice should first learn how to jump inside the long rope, without worrying about entering a moving rope. The jumper stands in the middle of the rope, facing one of the turners, hands loosely clasped together at the waist, and jumps slightly off the ground in a half-time rhythm. As with the short rope, the rebound occurs when the rope is overhead. For variety, the jumper may choose any of the footwork techniques taught with the short rope or create new ones.

ENTERING THE SINGLE LONG ROPE: FRONT DOOR ENTRANCE (DF = 1.1)

Figure 6.3

Two approaches are possible for entering a moving long rope. The easiest approach is referred to as "going in the front door." When the jumper is standing at the front door, the rope is going up when it is farthest away. To enter, the jumper stands near one of the turners and steps in just as the rope moves away. To assist the jumper with the entrance timing, the turners should give a verbal cue each time the rope hits the floor. For example, ". . . ready, ready, run."

The "back door" is a more difficult entrance (DF = 1.5). This time the jumper stands on the side from which the rope is going down when it is farthest away. The jumper enters as the rope reaches its apex and, unlike when going in the front door, must jump immediately upon entering.

EXITING: BACK DOOR EXIT (DF = 1.2)

Figure 6.4   **a**

b

To exit, the jumper steps out toward one of the turners immediately after jumping. In contrast to entering, exiting through the back door is easier than exiting through the front door; the jumper leaves on the side where the rope is going up, which gives the jumper more time to exit.

CANCAN (DF = 1.7)

Figure 6.5   **a**

The Cancan, which is the famous Rockette dance step, is another example of how the footwork techniques done with a short rope can also be done with a long rope. While jumping on, say, the left foot, the participant lifts the right knee up on the first jump. On the next jump, the jumper sets the right foot down briefly (not shown), and then

b

kicks up with the same foot on the third jump in the sequence. On the last jump in the sequence, the right foot is brought down so that the weight may be transferred to it. The jumper may now restart the sequence, but with the left knee lifting up. Note that it doesn't matter on which of the four jumps in the cycle the rope passes under.

180-DEGREE TURN-ABOUT (DF = 1.3)

Figure 6.6

a

b

The jumper jumps and turns 180 degrees to face the opposite direction. To begin, the student may wish to first practice turning only 90 degrees at a time.

360-DEGREE TURN-ABOUT (DF = 1.6)

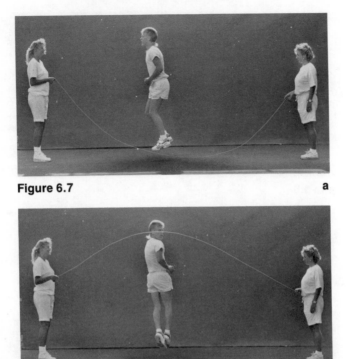

Figure 6.7

a

b

c

d

With this technique, the jumper makes a complete revolution, to end up facing the same direction as when she or he started. A higher jump and better balance is required than with the 180-Degree Turn-About.

WITH OTHER PROPS (DF = variable)

Figure 6.8   a

b

c

d

Other props are easily incorporated with the long rope because the jumper doesn't need to worry about turning the rope. The short rope, Hoppity Hop, pogo stick, and hula hoop are just some examples. Bouncing a ball or throwing beanbags between two jumpers are some other fun possibilities. Again, imagination is the limit. (Of course, be certain that the student has first mastered the prop without the jump rope.)

Double Dutch Techniques

All the techniques accomplished with the single long rope can also be accomplished with Double Dutch—where two long ropes rotate in an inward direction. Here are some tips for learning Double Dutch and some more ideas for students to create their own techniques.

DOUBLE DUTCH TURNING SKILLS (DF = 2.5)

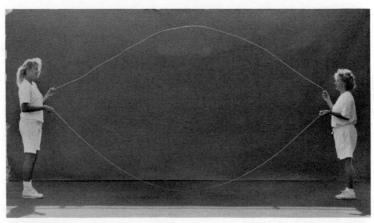

Figure 6.9   **a**

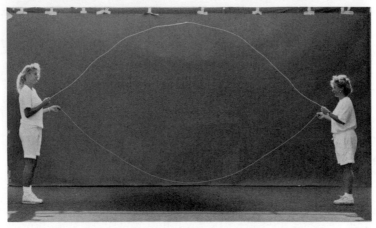

b

In Double Dutch, each rope is alternately turned inward so that one rope is at the apex while the other is at the bottom. As with the single long rope, the ropes are turned from the forearms with the elbows held close to the body.

ENTERING DOUBLE DUTCH (DF = 2.0)

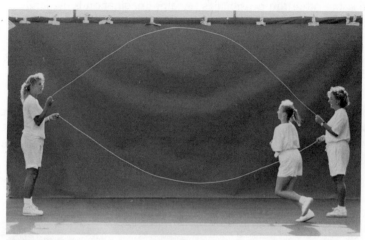

Figure 6.10

The jumper stands close to a turner and enters as the farthest rope touches the ground. The turners may give the verbal cue "One, two, ready, go!" The jumper must jump immediately upon entering.

TWO-FOOT JUMP (DF = 1.8)

Figure 6.11

As with single long rope jumping, the jumper holds both hands at the waist and jumps just high enough to clear the rope. The rhythm is now single time, however, because Double Dutch requires twice the jumping speed of the single long rope.

EXITING FROM DOUBLE DUTCH (DF = 2.3)

Figure 6.12   a

b

To anticipate exiting, the jumper should jump toward one turner. Immediately after jumping over the rope turned by the turner's right hand, the student exits close to the turner's left shoulder, or vice versa.

TURNERS JUMP WITH THE JUMPER (DF = VARIABLE)

Figure 6.13   a

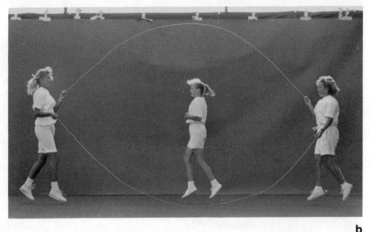

                                                                                                                   b

Skilled turners don't have to stand still while turning the rope. They can also complement many of the techniques being accomplished by the jumper, as in this example where all participants are doing Scissors.

PARTNER JUMPING (DF = VARIABLE)

Figure 6.14   a

b

c

d

Of course, there's plenty of room for more than one jumper in the middle of long ropes. Two or more jumpers can not only copy each other's techniques; they can also create partner dances, as exemplified here.

PART III

Using the Jump Rope in Physical Education

There's more to teaching rope jumping than showing how to measure a rope and execute techniques. The students should also know how and why a complete workout should be structured, from warm-up to cool-down. It's also important that they know how to adjust the intensity of their workouts with a jump rope to suit their current levels of fitness. In chapter 7 we'll cover these points and give you some practical tips for organizing your classes (and the students!).

An example of an eight-part jump rope unit is included in chapter 8. The sample unit strives to include variety, progressively more challenging skills, and both long- and short-term goals for motivation. Finally, chapter 9 describes various jump rope games and events that will stimulate your students' imaginations and keep them looking forward to their next jump rope class. Remember, the key to getting children hooked on exercise is to package and sell it as fun. This approach works well for adults also.

7
CHAPTER

Organizing Classes

It's important that rope jumping be as enjoyable for the instructor as it is for the students. Being able to organize the students, the classes, and the entire course are keys toward this end. In this chapter we look at the order and components of a typical jump rope class and their particular relevance.

Before the Class

Place groups of ropes in several locations along a wall or around the gym to avoid long lines when the students pick them up. You will find that having the ropes color-coded by length is especially helpful if you have students of different heights or if you are teaching several different grade levels (see page 15). Many manufacturers will color-code the ropes for you. If your ropes are indistinguishable, place pieces of colored tape on the handles to set the different lengths apart. Also have music with a strong beat selected to help motivate your students during the aerobic phase. Music with 120 to 140 beats per minute is especially helpful because this is the pace at which it is most comfortable to jump.

Setting Up Expectations: The Introduction

The jump rope has been around for centuries, and yet most people are still unfamiliar with the great variety of tricks and excitement it can generate. Therefore, to kick off your section on rope jumping it is helpful to arrange a viewing of a videotape on rope jumping in cooperation with the media specialist or classroom teacher. A companion

video to this book is available through Human Kinetics Publishers (see page 91). Videotapes are available from IRSO, from the American Heart Association if you plan to hold a Jump Rope For Heart event, and from some mail-order catalogs specializing in physical fitness. Another strategy guaranteed to raise students' excitement level is to invite a jump rope demonstration team to perform for the entire school.

Before each class, a brief positive explanation of what is to follow will focus students' attention on the upcoming goals. For example, "Today we are going to learn how to jump rope properly, just like boxers do! By the end of our course on rope jumping, you're going to know how to do many jump rope tricks that you will be able to show to your friends and parents. You are also going to learn how much fun fitness can be."

Organizing Students

The formations used for instructing students (see Figure 7.1) include squads, scattered, lines, circle, and semicircle. The formation you choose will depend on the facilities, the number of students, the activity, and your preference. In general, the scattered formation allows the greatest number of rope jumpers in a given area. Whatever formation you choose, be certain that it allows the students enough room to swing their ropes without striking their neighbors. Also, avoid formations that force you to teach with your back to the students.

Before sending the students to pick up their ropes, give them a task they must accomplish on their return to the formation. For example, "When you return to your space, make the first letter of your first name with the rope," or "Make a circle

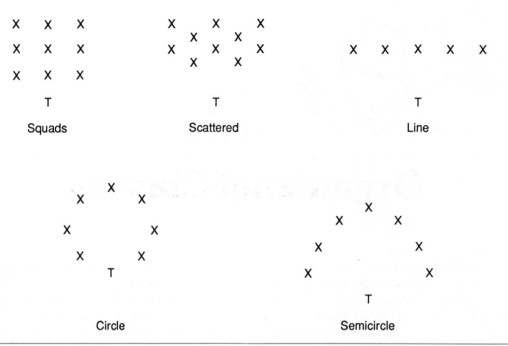

Figure 7.1 Some examples of student formations. *Note.* X = Student, T = Teacher.

with your rope and sit down inside the circle with the handles behind you." You might use one of the class members as an example, depending on age level. If you don't assign a task, pandemonium may ensue when the students begin playing with the ropes.

Components of the Actual Class

Each individual jump rope class is optimally comprised of five separate phases in the following order: warm-up, stretching, skill development, aerobic workout, and cool-down. Let's review the hows and whys of each phase.

Priming All Systems — The Warm-Up

Sudden increased demands in work intensity, range of motion, or skill pose much greater stress to the body, and hence greater risk of injury, than when those demands are gradually introduced (the graduation principle, again). For this reason a 5-minute warm-up necessarily precedes all active class sections.

The warm-up derives its name from the fact that the temperature of the body does actually increase with light exercise. Research indicates that warmed muscles are more elastic and therefore less prone to injury. The warm-up serves other purposes as well. Circulation to the muscles increases, which readies their metabolic machinery for the more intense work to follow, and heart and breathing rates also rise.

The warm-up serves one other function that is especially important for skilled activities like rope jumping—it primes the nervous system for the timing, rhythm, and coordination subtleties unique to the activity. Thus, we recommend that, except for the first class, the warm-up phase consist predominantly of Low-Impact Techniques and basic jumping rather than general movement like calisthenics or jogging.

Stretching It Out

Attaining flexibility is best achieved through stretching exercises. Static-type stretches, where a position is held for 15 to 30 seconds and repeated at least three times, is currently advocated over the pulse- or bounce-type stretching methods. Figures 7.2 through 7.10 illustrate several static stretches that are well suited for rope jumping. Remind the students to continue breathing normally through the stretch and to relax if they feel a burning sensation in the stretched muscle. There are several excellent books devoted to stretching (a few are listed in the bibliography), and the reader is referred to them if further information is desired.

TORSO STRETCH

Figure 7.2

The student stands with feet shoulder-width apart, toes forward, and knees slightly bent, folds the rope in half, and reaches both arms up with the elbows slightly bent. The student bends the torso gently to one side and holds, then slowly returns to center and repeats to the other side.

OVERHEAD SHOULDER STRETCH

Figure 7.3   a   b

The student stands with feet together and knees relaxed, folds the rope in quarters, and lifts both arms overhead as in Figure 7.3a. Then the student

slowly brings both arms back to the place that feels tight on top of the shoulders and holds this position, keeping the head and neck vertical and the elbows bent, as in Figure 7.3b.

BEHIND THE BACK SHOULDER STRETCH

Figure 7.4

Standing with feet shoulder-width apart and knees relaxed, the student folds the rope in half and places it behind the back, then gently bends the elbows and pulls up to feel the stretch in front of the shoulders, keeping the head and neck vertical and the elbows slightly flexed.

UPPER CALF (GASTROCNEMIUS) STRETCH

Figure 7.5

Standing with one foot in front of the other and torso leaning forward, the student places both hands on the forward bent thigh for balance, extends the back leg and keeps the back foot with the heel on the ground, with toes pointing forward and in line with the heel. The student shifts the body weight forward and holds this position, then slowly changes sides.

LOWER CALF (SOLEUS) STRETCH

Figure 7.6

Starting in the same position as for the Upper Calf Stretch, the student gently lifts the back heel off the floor allowing the back knee to bend, shifts the weight slightly onto the back leg and holds, then slowly changes sides.

FRONT OF HIP (HIP FLEXOR) STRETCH

Figure 7.7

Standing with one foot in front of the other and with the torso leaning forward, the student begins with the hands on the front thigh and slowly shifts the weight onto the ball of the back foot (as if lowering the hips down to the floor.) The hands can be placed on either side of the forward bent leg for a deep stretch. The ankle and knee of the forward bent leg are kept in one straight line, and the back knee is kept pointing down with the back heel up. The student changes sides slowly.

FRONT OF THIGH (QUADRICEPS) STRETCH

Figure 7.8

Assuming a forward lunge position with the toes and heels of each foot in line, the student places both hands on the thigh of the forward bent leg, slowly lowers the back knee down to the floor, allowing the back heel to lift off the floor and the hips to move forward, while keeping the upper back, hip, and knee of the back leg in one straight line.

INNER THIGH STRETCH

Figure 7.9

Standing with a wide stance, the student shifts the weight to one side and bends the knee on that side while bringing the torso forward, placing the hands on the ground in front for support and keeping the toes and heels in line with each other, then gently returns to center and stretches to the other side.

BACK OF THIGH (HAMSTRING) STRETCH

Figure 7.10

Standing with the feet under the hips, toes forward, and knees relaxed, the student curves the spine forward vertebra by vertebra, letting the weight of the head pull the spine down, places both arms behind the knees, and pulls the ribs to the thighs, keeping the ribs "glued" to *one* thigh, then slowly extends the other leg and feels the stretch in the back of this extended leg. The student then releases the extended leg and repeats the stretch on the other leg, slowly releasing the arms from behind the knees and lowering the hips while bending both knees, rolling through the spine, vertebra by vertebra, to come to a standing position. The neck should be kept relaxed while stretching, and students should not hold their breath.

Motor Skills Development

This is the phase where new techniques are introduced. If you are unable to demonstrate the technique yourself, have your students learn from the book, from an experienced student, or from an instructional video. Which techniques are taught will depend on how advanced your students are. By the way, many children will tell you that they know how to jump rope when they don't know how to do it properly. Be certain that they have the basics mastered as described in the technique section before introducing them to more advanced skills.

The Aerobic Phase — Using the Ropics Approach

Now it's time to work or play, depending on your perspective. Remember that continuous rope jumping is relatively strenuous, especially for novices. Therefore, inform the students that they should do Low-Impact Techniques, turn a long rope, or walk briskly whenever they become winded or their calves become tired, and begin jumping again when they have recovered.

A more formal method for monitoring and adjusting students' exercise intensity is to use the "Rated Perceived Exertion" (RPE) scale shown in Table 7.1. To use the RPE scale, which was developed by Dr. Gunnar Borg, the participant exercises to maintain a sense of exertion between 3 (moderate) and 5-6 (strong) on a scale of 0 to 10. If the participant is unable to talk comfortably while jumping, they are definitely exerting themselves beyond level 6 and should discontinue jumping until they feel comfortable again. You might find it helpful to post a large RPE scale on a wall for the students' reference.

Table 7.1 Rated Perceived Exertion (RPE) Scale

0	Nothing at all
0.5	Extremely slight
1	Very slight
2	Slight
3	Moderate
4	Somewhat strong
5	Strong
6	
7	Very strong
8	
9	Extremely strong
10	Maximal

Note. From G.V. Borg, "Psychophysical Bases of Perceived Exertion," *Medicine and Science in Sports and Exercise,* **14**, p. 378, 1982, © by The American College of Sports Medicine. Reprinted by permission.

To set the tone for this workout part of the class, you might try any one or more of the following strategies:

• Put on a record or tape and let the students turn and jump their ropes to the entire song. As their ability with a rope improves, they may be able to jump rope through two or more songs.
• The students can also count the rope revolutions as they jump. This strategy lets them see how much they improve during the course. More advanced students may prefer to see how many of a certain trick they can do consecutively.

- There are many jump rope games that can be done with or without music (see chapter 9).

Cooling Off

Surprisingly, the most strenuous part of a patient's cardiac treadmill stress test is when he or she lies down abruptly at the end of the exercise period. Suddenly, the heart no longer receives assistance from the large skeletal muscles' contractions, and it must vigorously pump the blood alone. Cooling down gradually, then, is an important habit to acquire. End the class with the easier games, Low-Impact Techniques and basic jumping, or other light exercises.

Summary

As you become experienced and comfortable with teaching rope jumping, you'll discover that there are innumerable ways to make each class unique and intriguing for your students. Once the students become acquainted with rope jumping, their own creativity will also become a constant source of inspiration for you. To help you get started, we have put together an eight-part rope jumping unit that incorporates the principles we've discussed previously.

8 CHAPTER

A Sample Eight-Lesson Rope Jumping Unit

To give teachers more flexibility we have outlined, rather than detailed, eight lessons for a unit on rope jumping. Some of the factors that will determine how you administer the lessons are the size of your facility, the ages of your students, their experience with rope jumping, class length, and any special education needs. The lessons assume that you have the necessary basic background or training in teaching and directing children. Please alter the plans as needed to work for you.

Lesson 1 (Short Rope)

Note. The lessons assume that you have prepared the students as outlined earlier in the book. They should know what length of rope to select and how to turn the rope and jump properly.

Set-Up
Have students pick up ropes and take positions in a scattered formation.

Warm-Up
Allow students several minutes of basic jumping or calisthenics (no advanced tricks or speed jumping, even if some students are already experienced).

Stretching
Depending on the length of your class period, spend at least 3 to 5 minutes on stretching. You may choose to use some of the stretches illustrated on pages 63 through 65.

Lesson
Introduce three or four basic techniques by demonstrating or describing them as best you can (e.g., Windmill, Figure-Eight, Skier, and Twist).

Review the Rated Perceived Exertion Scale; remind students that they can adjust exercise intensity by mixing Low-Impact Techniques like Windmills and Figure-Eights with jumping techniques. Allow several minutes of practice. If one student has a technique particularly well mastered, have him or her show the rest of the class.

Teach two additional basic techniques (e.g., Bell and Swing Wrap).

Practice
Put on music and let students work at their own paces on the techniques. You can assign helpers or assist individually while the rest of the class jumps.

Cool-Down
End the class with a short game, activity, or relay that all students enjoy. Games like Clean Your Own Back Yard, Stuck in the Mud, and Last Flag Pulled are described in books like *Awesome Elementary School Physical Education Activities* by Cliff Carnes (see the bibliography). Any students who might have been frustrated with rope jumping will leave feeling good after a fun activity with which they are familiar.

Lesson 2 (Short Rope)

Set-Up
Have students pick up ropes as they enter the gym and take positions in a scattered formation.

Warm-Up
Warm up with several minutes of easy jumping and Low-Impact Techniques.

Stretching
Spend at least 3 to 5 minutes stretching.

Review

Put on music and let students review the techniques they learned in Lesson 1.

Lesson

Introduce three or four new techniques, including at least one Low-Impact Technique—for instance, Run Step, Jogging Step, Foot Catch, and Leg Over Pass.

Practice

Once again, turn on the music and allow the students to practice any of the techniques introduced so far. Encourage them to ask you or other students for help. *Try* should be the key word for the day. Remind the students about using the Rated Perceived Exertion Scale.

Take a couple of minutes to have students come out in the middle of the gym and show off their skills.

Cool-Down

Wrap up the class with a jump rope game or activity that all students can participate in. You might select games that use the rope but don't require repetitive jumping, such as High Water, Low Water or Jump Over the Brook (see chapter 9).

When time allows, end class with a cool-down period of 3 to 5 minutes of walking, light stretching, or a combination of the two. A soft-sounding record played at low volume adds a nice touch.

Lesson 3
(Short and Long Single Ropes)

Set-Up

Have students pick up ropes as they enter the gym and take positions in a scattered formation.

Warm-Up

Warm up with several minutes of easy jumping and Low-Impact Techniques.

Stretching

Spend 3 to 5 minutes stretching.

Review

Devote 5 to 10 minutes reviewing what has been presented in Lessons 1 and 2. This is your chance to walk around and assist the students experiencing difficulty. Encourage their progress, as this is often a critical time in their learning process.

Lesson

Divide the class into groups of three or four. Teach

how to turn the single long rope (see page 47). Students should stand far enough apart so that a 6- to 10-inch segment of the long rope touches the floor. Prompt the students to turn the ropes in unison by using verbal cues if necessary, such as "One, two, ready, turn."

Teach how to jump over the long rope. The jumper can either stand in the middle and begin jumping when the rope comes around, or enter the front door, as described on page 48.

Practice

Allow the students to take turns and practice for the rest of the class period. Experienced long rope jumpers may learn new techniques or assist beginners. Assist and encourage.

Cool-Down

When time allows, end class with a cool-down period of 3 to 5 minutes of walking, light stretching, or a combination of the two. A soft-sounding record played at low volume adds a nice touch.

Lesson 4
(Short and Long Single Ropes)

Set-Up

Have students pick up ropes as they enter the gym and take positions in a scattered formation.

Warm-Up

Warm up with several minutes of easy jumping and Low-Impact Techniques.

Stretching

Spend 3 to 5 minutes stretching.

Review

Review short rope techniques and possibly introduce two or three additional techniques, such as Side Straddle, Front Straddle, and Forearm Wrap.

Lesson

Have the students form teams of two or three, and encourage them to develop a short routine from the techniques they have already learned. They might repeat each technique three or four times before continuing to the next technique. Set a time limit on the routines so that every group or individual will have a chance to showcase their creation during the last class of the unit. Play upbeat music to enhance their creativity.

Review long rope techniques. Introduce the use of the short rope inside the long rope. You can also encourage students to jump together inside the long rope.

Introduce the use of other props inside the long rope, such as jumpers tossing a ball or beanbag between them.

Practice

Allow time for practice and for students to use their imaginations with either the long or short rope. Assist and encourage.

Cool-Down

When time allows, end class with a cool-down period of 3 to 5 minutes of walking, light stretching, or a combination of the two. A soft-sounding record played at low volume adds a nice touch.

Lesson 5 (Short Rope, Long Single Rope, and Double Dutch)

Note. Children under the third- or fourth-grade level typically do not have the motor skills necessary to learn Double Dutch. If your group is not ready to do Double Dutch, take the extra time to develop earlier skills or learn other techniques from chapters 5 and 6.

Set-Up

Have students pick up ropes as they enter the gym and take positions in a scattered formation.

Warm-Up

Warm up with several minutes of easy jumping and Low-Impact Techniques.

Stretching

Spend 3 to 5 minutes stretching.

Review

Allow practice and review time. Encourage students to further develop the freestyle routine from Lesson 4. They may also choose to develop individual routines.

Lesson

Introduce additional short rope techniques, such as Toe and Heel Touches, Knee Lifts, and Waist Wrap.

Introduce Double Dutch. First teach proper rope-turning technique as described on page 53. A good deal of time is often needed to master this skill. Rotate turners because some students have difficulty turning with certain people, especially

when learning. Patience and encouragement are required at this stage.

Demonstrate entering into Double Dutch and basic jumping as described on page 54.

Practice

Allow students to practice turning, entering, and jumping Double Dutch. Patience and encouragement will be required at this stage.

Cool-Down

When time allows, end class with a cool-down period of 3 to 5 minutes of walking, light stretching, or a combination of the two. A soft-sounding record played at low volume adds a nice touch.

Lesson 6 (Short Rope and Double Dutch)

Set-Up

Have students pick up ropes as they enter the gym and take positions in a scattered formation.

Warm-Up

Warm up with several minutes of easy jumping and Low-Impact Techniques.

Stretching

Spend 3 to 5 minutes stretching.

Review

Much of this lesson can be spent reviewing the Double Dutch activities. As some of the students begin to master Double Dutch, have them demonstrate in front of their classmates.

Lesson

Introduce the use of other techniques in Double Dutch (see pages 55-57). Practice with upbeat music.

You might also introduce several intriguing, more advanced techniques, such as Front Cross, 180-Degree Turn-About, Matador Whirl, and Open Step-Through.

Practice

Allow practice and review time. Don't forget the music, and remind students to monitor exercise intensity. Encourage and assist them with their techniques and routines.

Cool-Down

When time allows, end class with a cool-down period of 3 to 5 minutes of walking, light stretching, or a combination of the two. A soft-sounding record played at low volume adds a nice touch.

Lesson 7 (Short Rope, Long Single Rope, and Double Dutch)

Set-Up
Have students pick up ropes as they enter the gym and take positions in a scattered formation.

Warm-Up
Warm up with several minutes of easy jumping and Low-Impact Techniques.

Stretching
Spend 3 to 5 minutes stretching.

Review
Provide a review time with music. Encourage students to polish their techniques and routines for the big show during the next lesson. Remind them of the previously set time limit for each routine.

Lesson
Introduce the use of other props that can be used with short ropes, long ropes, or Double Dutch, such as pogo sticks, Hoppity Hops, hula hoops, basketballs, pogo balls, and so on (see pages 52-53). (Be certain that the students have first mastered the prop without the jump rope.) Allow frequent changes between turners and jumpers. What's important is not that they master every possibility but rather that their imaginations be sparked so that they will continue to experiment and practice on their own during recess or at home.

Practice
Devote several minutes to allowing the students to practice doing a chosen jumping technique as many times in a row as they can without missing. Another objective could be to jump as many times as possible in 30 seconds.

Cool-Down
When time allows, end class with a cool-down period of 3 to 5 minutes of walking, light stretching, or a combination of the two. A soft-sounding record played at low volume adds a nice touch.

Lesson 8 (The Grand Finale)

Set-Up
Have students pick up ropes as they enter the gym and take positions in a scattered formation.

Warm-Up
Warm up with several minutes of easy jumping and Low-Impact Techniques.

Stretching
Spend 3 to 5 minutes stretching.

Finale
Make a large circle and have the students "strut their stuff!" If possible, videotape their routines for later review. Students can perform for the class either individually or with their group. They can use any of the rope tricks or props introduced throughout the unit. Be sure to enforce the previously set time limit on each routine so everyone gets a chance.

Children love to see themselves on video. If there is time, show the tape at the end of class. Save the video and use it at a PTA meeting, physical education activity night, awards day, and so on.

See chapter 9 for other ideas about activities you and your class can do during or following the unit.

Evaluation

Construct any type of evaluation that fits your situation. If the students can handle a written exam, you can put together a little quiz, selecting a format that is best for you and your students. A final routine of 6 to 10 tricks could be required, using a list of 15 from which students can select. They could show you their techniques on a day designated for testing. How you score or determine a value system for your test will again be determined by the age and ability level of the groups you are working with.

9
CHAPTER

Games and Events

The greatest challenge facing physical educators is to motivate their students to exercise on a regular basis throughout life. Research has shown that former athletes who ceased being active eventually acquired the same health problems as those who never exercised regularly. It is also well established that people, including children, respond better to positive reinforcement (reward) than to negative reinforcement (punishment). Therefore, making the exercise experience as rewarding as possible will achieve much better results than repeated warnings about the punishment to come if they don't exercise (heart disease, decreased vigor, osteoporosis, etc.).

Educators must also consider what their students want or expect from exercise. Individual adults might exercise to lose weight, improve their endurance, better their performance in another sport, meet other active people, and so forth. Most children, however, simply want to have fun and play with other children. Fortunately, rope jumping is inherently enjoyable and lends itself well to a great variety of games, competitions, and events. That characteristic, more than its ability to "make bodies strong in 12 different ways," is what is usually important to children. Later, as they mature and become more concerned about appearance, performance, health, or fitness, they will already be

confident and feel good about an exercise that does it all.

Games

Commensurate with rope jumping's long and multicultural history, hundreds of games have been created by hundreds of imaginative minds. The following games, which can usually be done with either long or short ropes, are only a small sample. With a little imagination you and your students will come up with more variations.

Rhymes

Probably the best known jump rope game is to jump to the tempo of singsong rhymes. Of the hundreds of rhymes and variations popular for rope jumping, two are given on page 72. The bibliography lists two books that give even more rhymes: *Jump Rope!* by P. Skolnick, and *Aerobic Rope Skipping* by P. Smith. Of course, you can also substitute music for rhymes. The objective might be to jump as long as possible without missing, or to complete one verse before allowing another participant or group of participants to jump.

"Johnny Over the Ocean"

Johnny over the ocean,
Johnny over the sea.
Johnny broke the milk bottle
and blamed it on me.
I told Ma. Ma told Pa.
Johnny got a licking,
Ha, Ha, Ha.
How many lickings did he get?
1, 2, 3 . . .

"Mama, Mama"

Mama, Mama, I am sick,
Send for the doctor, quick, quick, quick.
Mama, Mama, turn around.
Mama, Mama, touch the ground.
Mama, Mama, are you lame?
Mama, Mama, spell your name.
Mama, Mama has much to do.
Mama, Mama, are you through?

(The participant does the actions suggested in each line and runs out of the rope on the last line.)

Hot Peppers

The idea with Hot Peppers, also known as Hot Bricks in some areas of the country, is to jump as fast as possible in a given amount of time or until the jumper misses. Hot Peppers can also be integrated into the end of a rhyme such as "Johnny Over the Ocean."

High Water, Low Water

In this game, the long rope is not twirled in a circle, but swung back and forth in an arc as a number of participants jump to clear the rope. Initially, the rope is swung low to the ground, and then gradually raised higher and higher until only one person is able to clear the rope.

Higher and Higher

The same idea as with High Water, Low Water, but the rope is swung in a complete circle.

Jump Over the Brook

Place two ropes lengthwise about 2 feet apart on the ground. The students take turns jumping over the ropes, pretending a brook runs between them. Widen the ropes after every student has had a chance to jump. The student who jumps over the widest "brook" stays dry and wins.

Formations

Formations could be considered an obstacle course of long ropes that the participants must successfully negotiate. At each station, the student must do a certain technique or routine for a set number of times. The students may also compete against each other to see which individual or team can successfully negotiate a particular formation the fastest. Figure 9.1 illustrates three possible formations. The variations are endless. Of course, allow the turners to trade with the jumpers at some point, so they can have fun, too.

Tag

Children can also play a form of Tag by using formations that incorporate only long ropes. Two students run through the ropes, one chasing the other. They must enter and exit without missing. A runner who misses must take one end of the rope, and the relieved turner takes that person's place. If the chaser tags the other, they switch roles. In another variation of Tag, Figure-Eight Tag, the one who is "it" chases the other student in a figure-eight pattern around and through one long rope or Double Dutch ropes.

Follow the Leader

A leader is chosen to challenge the rest of the group to successfully complete a technique anywhere from one to three times in a row. A routine of several techniques may also be used. Individuals in the group then have anywhere from one to three tries to accomplish what the leader has done. The process continues until there is one follower left, and that follower then becomes the new leader. If the leader fails to successfully complete a technique he or she intended, then the first person who failed becomes the new leader.

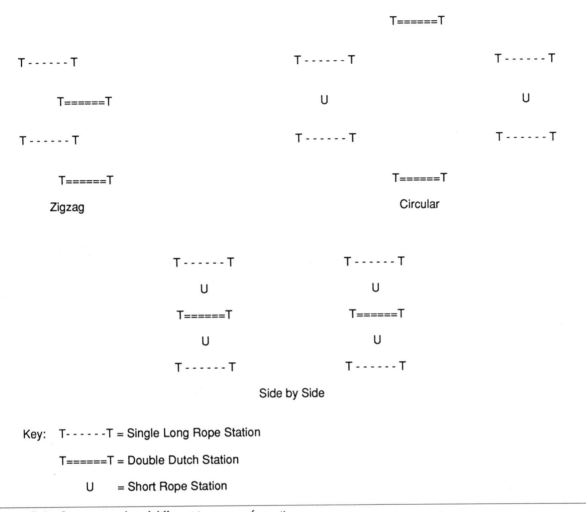

Figure 9.1   Some examples of different jump rope formations.

Simon Says

This game is the same as Follow the Leader except that the followers also must quit if they do a technique the leader demonstrates without saying "Simon says."

Tournaments

A well-run jump rope tournament can be greatly motivating for students—it gives them concrete objectives to strive for and a deadline to anticipate. The primary intent of competition must be to better one's own athletic, emotional, and social skills, and not to find out who is the "best."

One of the advantages of rope jumping is that there is such a diversity of skills to master that it is difficult for any one participant to be the best at everything. Thus, a child can excel at a particular aspect of rope jumping and reap the confidence and image building needed. For example, Paul turns the rope faster than anyone, while nobody does Crosses as consistently as Jenny, and Michael is considered the master of Step-Through combinations. If you have a child who learns more slowly than the rest, a good approach is to give that child a particular technique, routine, or skill all his or her own to master; the child can then showcase it before the group when ready. This gives such children their own areas of distinction. Perhaps nothing squelches a child's enthusiasm for exercise faster than having the negative distinction of being consistently "last." This should never happen!

Another appealing aspect of jump rope competition is that you don't have to pit child against child or team against team. Instead, you can simply challenge the children to master a prop. Their success then rests solely on themselves and not on the talents and fair play of their opponents. With the single rope, children can also develop their skills at their own paces rather than being forced to measure up immediately to their teammates or opponents.

The possible objectives in rope jumping are nearly endless. Nevertheless, most competitions in both short and long rope jumping fall under one of four categories.

Endurance

The Guinness World Record for basic rope jumping is now over 36 hours! (All right, the rules do allow a 5-minute break every hour.) Of course, school or class records will not be so stratospheric, but the Guinness record does emphasize that proficient enthusiasts can do basic rope jumping techniques such as the Jogging Step for a great while. Therefore, most endurance competitions rely on doing more advanced techniques with the single short rope such as Double Unders (see the epilogue) and even Triples. These techniques are quite intense and limit individual attempts to minutes and usually seconds.

Of course, nonadvanced rope jumpers will have difficulties with such demanding techniques, and less strenuous techniques may be chosen, such as Side Straddles or Crosses. The object might be to do the most in a row, or to go for the longest period of time. Misses might or might not be allowed. It is also permissible to have children challenge each other in teams, with the team that does the technique the longest or the most consecutive times being the winner.

Speed

In speed jumping with either the long or single rope, the objective is to jump the most times possible in a given period of time. A time limit of 30 to 120 seconds is usually chosen, because the energy costs increase rapidly beyond 150 jumps per minute. Any jumping technique may be chosen, although fancy footwork should be avoided because sprained ankles are more apt to occur at fast rates.

Speed jumping is also demanding on the judges who are trying to accurately count the churning feet. For races using the Jogging Step, a common counting method is to only note when the right foot touches the ground and then multiply by two. For Crosses, count only when the arms cross each other and then multiply by two. Some judges count mentally, while others use clickers.

Compulsories

In compulsories, participants are required to do certain basic or intermediate techniques in sequence. Points are subtracted for each miss or failure to accomplish the technique. Although the other competition options can stand alone, compulsories are usually a part of a greater tournament, because more than one participant typically obtains a perfect score. The compulsory format used by IRSO (see pages 75-76) is one of many variations that can be employed.

Freestyle

All-around freestyle competition is the most challenging and potentially the most rewarding for both participant and spectator alike. Freestyle rope jumping relies not on pure athleticism, but on a wide variety of skills, creativity, problem solving, and, with partner or long rope jumping, the ultimate in teamwork.

Participants choreograph their own routines, which should fit a certain time limit (usually 45 to 90 seconds). Certain techniques may or may not be required to be included. It should also be decided whether other props such as pogo sticks or hula hoops are allowed to be incorporated. If logistics allow, musical accompaniment can spur creativity and add another dimension of excitement to the routines.

Freestyle competition is also challenging for judges, who must weigh originality, execution, and degree of difficulty. Obviously, freestyle is the most subjective of the competitions, and it is especially helpful to have more than one judge.

An outline of the tournament format used by IRSO follows. IRSO Double Dutch competition is similar to the format used by the American Double Dutch League. For further information on rules, score sheets, judging, and physical setup, contact the respective organizations at the addresses listed in chapter 1.

International Rope Skipping Organization Tournament Outline

In IRSO competitions, participants are divided according to grades. Teams, not individuals, compete and consist of two to five members of either gender. The following are the different events in the regional and international tournaments.

Short Rope Events

In each of the short rope competitions, participants compete both alone and with partners.

Single Compulsory

Techniques (or "tricks") must be completed in the following order within 30 seconds. Points are deducted for each technique missed or done out of order.

2 Forward Front Crosses

2 Forward Matador Crosses (1 each side)

180-Degree Turn-About

2 Backward Front Crosses

2 Backward Matador Crosses (1 each side)

180-Degree Turn-About

10 Cancans (5 each leg, alternating legs)

Double Compulsory

The same techniques listed above must be done in unison by two team members within 40 seconds. Points are deducted for techniques missed, done out of order, or not executed in unison.

Single Speed

The object is to jump as fast as possible, using the Jogging Step, for 60 seconds. Only the right foot is counted, for all speed competitions.

Double Speed

One of two team members jumps as many times as possible, using the Jogging Step, for 30 seconds. At the end of the period, the other member immediately jumps as many times as possible in 30 seconds. The counts are added together.

Single Freestyle

A participant performs a routine of her or his own creation that lasts 45 to 60 seconds. Penalties accrue for routines of longer or shorter durations. The participant is judged on execution, creativity, symmetry (ability to do techniques on each side), and continuity.

Double Freestyle

Two team members perform a routine of their own creation that lasts 45 to 60 seconds. The techniques need not be performed in unison during the routine. As above, the team is judged on execution, creativity, symmetry, and continuity.

Double Dutch Events

In each of the Double Dutch events, two turners (or "enders") and one or two jumpers work together as a team. Turners and jumpers may exchange roles between the different events.

Single Compulsory

The participant executes the following Double Dutch techniques in sequence and within 35 seconds. Points are deducted as in the single rope events.

Proper entrance

2 360-Degree Turn-Abouts in one direction

2 360-Degree Turn-Abouts in the opposite direction

2 Side Straddles

2 Forward Straddles

8 Cancans (4 each leg, alternating legs)

Exit

Double Compulsory

Two team members execute, in sequence and in unison, the techniques listed for the Double Dutch single compulsory. The routine must be completed within 45 seconds. Points are deducted as above.

Single Speed

The participant jumps as many times possible in 2 minutes, using the Jogging Step. Only the right foot is counted.

Double Speed

One team member completes as many jumps possible in 1 minute, using the Jogging Step. After the first member exits, the second team member immediately enters and completes as many jumps possible in the second minute.

Single Freestyle

The participant performs a routine of her or his own creation that lasts 30 to 60 seconds. The routine is judged on creativity, continuity, difficulty, execution, symmetry, and turner involvement. Points are deducted if the routine is shorter or longer than 30 to 60 seconds.

Double Freestyle

Two team members perform a routine of their own creation lasting 30 to 60 seconds. The routine is judged similarly to the Double Dutch single freestyle competition, with the added consideration of how well the team members work together.

Note. From International Rope Skipping Organization Rules Committee (1986). *The Official I.R.S.O. Tournament Rules and Regulations*, Boulder, CO. Reprinted with permission of Richard Cendali.

Noncompetitive Events

Noncompetitive events can be just as appealing to kids as tournaments, and the following are just a few examples of the events to which rope jumping is well suited. Before deciding which event to organize, decide how much time you wish to devote to it. Events can be relatively simple, requiring only a few hours of your time to set up, or large and sophisticated, requiring the talents and time of committees and volunteers.

Fund-Raising

The AHA's Jump Rope For Heart event (see chapter 1) is the granddaddy of all rope jumping events. The advantage of Jump Rope For Heart for educators is the support, guidance, and materials your local AHA can offer.

In Jump Rope For Heart, children enlist sponsors who are willing to donate a small amount of money for each minute the child or the child's team jumps rope. An upper time limit is set so that the children don't overexert themselves and become injured or exhausted. The limit also lets the donors know what their maximum contribution would be. To further motivate the fund-raisers, incentives such as T-shirts, jump ropes, pins, and so forth, are offered to those who participate.

Talent Show

The great variety of routines possible, and its compatibility with music, makes rope jumping the perfect vehicle for children to show off their skills and creativity. Routines might feature choreographed routines with long or short ropes, use of other props such as Hoppity Hops, or special costumes; the children are quite free to be imaginative. You will need to set a time limit for each routine, however, to be certain everyone has a chance to perform. Talent shows can be great fun with the right group of students, and they require relatively little time from the organizer.

Demonstrations

If you have a group of talented, dedicated, and disciplined students, and you enjoy challenges, you might consider organizing a jump rope demonstration team. Literally hundreds of teams exist around the country, many sponsored by the AHA. The showmanship, agility, and daring of these jump rope wunderkinds make them in great demand at schools, health clubs, shopping malls, fairs, conventions, trade shows, parades, and nearly any other venue imaginable. For more information on how to organize a demonstration team, contact your local American Heart Association office.

Summary

An impressive variety of jump rope games and events complement the incredible variety of possible jump rope techniques. Take full advantage of options like Simon Says, talent shows, and friendly competitions to prove to your students that the path to fitness can be rewarding to the mind and emotions as well as the body. If this is not proven to them, few will have the discipline to make a commitment to lifelong exercise.

EPILOGUE

Further Insights Into Rope Jumping

If pressed to come up with one word describing the jump rope, we would have to say *versatile*. The jump rope is versatile in developing different areas of fitness, versatile in climate, facility, and travel requirements, and versatile in applications—whether it's used for gaining fitness, conditioning for sports, challenging competition, having fun on the playground, or entertaining an audience.

But perhaps the jump rope's incredible versatility is best illustrated by the immense variety of possible jumping techniques and variations. The jump rope family tree depicted in Figure E.1 indicates various types of rope jumping, and *The Jump Rope Primer* has illuminated only a few leaves from several of its branches. On one branch sprout techniques in which a single rope is shared by two people; on another branch, those in which a single person jumps over two ropes being turned by four people. As we've seen in *The Primer*, one large branch does not require any jumping at all.

We anticipate revealing more about this diverse tree, and further exploring its roots as well as its branches, at a later date. But for now, we'll leave you with a brief look at a few more leaves.

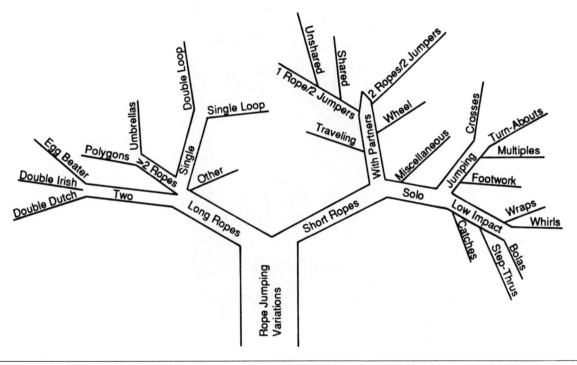

Figure E.1 This tree depicts the major variations of rope jumping.

DOUBLE UNDERS

Figure E.2

With Double Unders the rope turns *twice* for each jump rather than the usual single revolution. Triples, Quadruples, and even Quintuples are also possible.

ROPE TOSS

Figure E.3

Hundreds of other Low-Impact Techniques exist besides the ones illustrated in *The Primer*. The Rope Toss is one example.

SHOULDER WRAP

Figure E.4

It is also possible to mix techniques from other disciplines with the jump rope. The Shoulder Wrap is adapted from a technique used with the nunchaku—a weapon used in karate.

PARTNER ROPE JUMPING

Figure E.5

Team jumping is also possible with the short rope, as depicted here.

THE WHEEL

Figure E.6

The Wheel is a visually interesting variation that also challenges the jumpers because the arms must turn independently of each other.

DOUBLE DUTCH WITH GYMNASTICS

Figure E.7

Other disciplines can also be integrated with long ropes. Expert Double Dutchers aren't always content with just walking into the ropes.

EGG BEATER WITH A SHORT ROPE

Figure E.8

Talk about teamwork! The Egg Beater requires as many players as a basketball team.

Bibliography

Alter, J. (1986). *Stretch & Strengthen*. Boston: Houghton Mifflin.

Anderson, B. (1985). *Stretching*. Bolinas, CA: Shelter.

Baker, J. (1968). Comparison of rope skipping and jogging as methods of improving cardiovascular efficiency of college men. *Research Quarterly*, **39**, 240-243.

Borg, G. (1985). *An Introduction to Borg's RPE-scale*. Ithaca, NY: Mouvement.

Carnes, C. (1983). *Awesome Elementary School Physical Education Activities*. Carmichael, CA: Education.

Cendali, R. (1977). *Skip It for Fun*. Boulder, CO: Richard Cendali.

Getchell, B., & Cleary, C. (1980). The caloric cost of rope skipping and running. *The Physician and Sportsmedicine*, **7**, 56-60.

Hanson, M.R., Torrence, T., Hungerford, C.W., Smith, P., & Cendali, R. (1983). *Jump for the Health of It*. Dallas, TX: American Heart Association.

Jette, M., Mongeon, J., & Routhier, R. (1979). Energy cost of rope skipping. *Journal of Sports Medicine and Physical Fitness*, **19**, 33-37.

Kalbfleisch, S. (1985). *Jump!* New York: William Morrow.

Melson, B., & Worrel, V. (1986). *Rope Skipping for Fun and Fitness*. Witchita, KS: Woodlawn.

McArdle, W., Katch, F., & Katch, V. (1986). *Exercise Physiology: Energy, Nutrition and Human Performance*. Philadelphia, PA: Lea & Febiger.

Nike, Inc. (1988). Sport research review. *The Physician and Sportsmedicine*, **16**, Special advertising section.

Paffenbarger, R., Jr., Hyde, R., & Wing, A. (1986). Physical activity, all cause mortality, and longevity of college alumni. *New England Journal of Medicine*, **314**, 605-613.

Smith, P. (1981). *Aerobic Rope Skipping*. Freeport, NY: Educational Activities.

Skolnick, P. (1974). *Jump Rope!* New York, NY: Workman.

Solis, K., Foster, C., Thompson, N., & Cefalu, C. (1988). Aerobic requirements for and heart rate responses to variations in rope jumping techniques. *The Physician and Sportsmedicine*, **16**, 121-128.

Sutherland, M., & Carnes, C. (1987). *Awesome Jump Rope Activities Book*. Carmichael, CA: Education.

Index

From the Basic Two-Foot Jump to Double Dutch

A great companion to the book, *The Jump Rope Primer Video* is a tool that makes it easy for you to teach rope jumping to your students. Authors Ken Solis and Bill Budris use an easy-to-understand format to present all the jump rope techniques in *The Jump Rope Primer*, including

- short rope,
- long rope, and
- Double Dutch.

Plus, important concepts from the book are repeated here, such as preferred floor surfaces and how to control exercise intensity.

The video features school-age kids having fun and developing aerobic fitness through rope jumping while they demonstrate proper techniques. Skills begin with jumping properly without a rope; after students have mastered that, they learn to jump rhythmically, hold and turn the rope properly, and finally combine all the skills. From there, it's an easy progression to advanced techniques that are challenging and fun! You'll see the techniques choreographed into exciting routines to help motivate your students.

Make rope jumping a part of your curriculum. It's a fun and easy way for students to become physically fit. And with *The Jump Rope Primer Video*, it's easy for you to teach, too!

KEN M. SOLIS • BILL BUDRIS

F55

Ken Solis, MD, and Bill Budris

1991 • Approx 35 minutes • Item MSOL0189
ISBN 0-87322-325-X • $49.95 ($62.50 Canadian)

Save money by ordering *The Jump Rope Primer* and *The Jump Rope Primer Video* together!

Special book and video package!
Item MSOL01889 • $54.94 ($68.50 Canadian)

Human Kinetics Videos
A Division of Human
Kinetics Publishers, Inc

7920